THE ADVENTURES OF
Stout Mama

Other books by Sibyl James

In China with Harpo and Karl (Calyx Books, 1990)
Vallarta Street (Laughing Dog Press, 1988)
The White Junk of Love, Again (Calyx Books, 1986)

THE ADVENTURES OF
Stout Mama

SIBYL JAMES

Papier-Mache Press · Watsonville, California

First Edition

Cover art, "Dancing Solo," © 1992 by Isabel Sim-Hamilton

Cover design by Cynthia Heier

Photo by Karen DeWinter

Typography by Metro Typography

Grateful acknowledgment is made to the following publications which first published or accepted for publication some of the material in this book:

Gulf Stream Magazine, No. 4, 1991, for "The Gym," "Star Date," "Mick Jagger's Birthday," "Fourth of July Flags," and "Reasons for Travel"; *Hurricane Alice: A Feminist Quarterly*, Vol. 8, No. 2, Summer 1991, for "Literary Weight Loss"; *Caprice*, October 1991, for "The Student," "Ma's Cow," and "Platform Boots"; *Gulf Stream Magazine*, No. 6, 1992, for "Dislocated Soldiers" and "The Spirit Trap"; *Calyx: A Journal of Art and Literature by Women*, Vol. 14, No. 1, Summer 1992, for "Stout Mama and the Black Orchid Man"; *Caprice*, January 1993, for "Super Bowl Eagles"; *Eating Our Hearts Out: Women and Food* (Crossing Press), 1993, for "Literary Weight Loss"; *The Return of Women's Glib: The World's Best Women's Humor* (Crossing Press), 1994, for "High School Sex"; and *Ergo!*, June 1993, for "Cigarettes and Mayonnaise" and "Failing Nirvana."

Hardcover edition catalogued as follows:
Library of Congress Cataloging-in-Publication Data

James, Sibyl.
    The adventures of Stout Mama / Sibyl James. — 1st ed.
        p.   cm.
    ISBN 0-918949-34-3 (hardcover) : $14.00.
    1. Women college teachers—United States—Fiction.   I. Title.
PS3560.A396A66 1993   93-18338
813' .54—dc20   CIP

Thanks to Lady Eliza and Star, my computer and printer, in whose antique and capable hands Stout Mama was born.

Contents

THE ADVENTURES OF

Stout Mama

Stout Mama and the Nightmare Preface

*N*ormally, Stout Mama does not read prefaces. She dislikes wading through them, like entering her city's lake from the shore where the shallow water is topped with oil slicks left by power boats, and the long green fingers of milfoil weed snarl her thighs. She heads for the pier instead, stepping directly off it into the swim, the fresh deep currents of the story.

But lately Stout Mama has been battling insomnia. And so she's taken to reading prefaces, a soporific she's found more effective than warm milk or whiskey, and happily nonfattening.

Normally, Stout Mama avoids authors. She does not lionize them at parties or stand in line to get their autograph in books. She thinks authors like to talk about themselves too much. Stout Mama considers authors boring. She believes only a mother could love one. Prefaces, she feels, resemble authors. Autobiographical for yawning pages.

Stout Mama has learned that the favored style of prefaces is rumination. Some do this placidly, reminiscing like a cow in a spring field, chewing cud. Others are curmudgeonish. The worst are academic, heavy with the latest scholarly paradigms. Read too many of those, Stout Mama thinks, and her gall bladder could develop stones.

Tonight, Stout Mama has once again yawned off in the middle of a ruminative sentence. Normally, her post-preface slumbers are sound. But this time she has a nightmare: she dreams she has to write a preface. There she is at her worktable, chain-smoking, twisting her hair. She feels punished. She feels like her childhood self kept in at recess. She remembers being forced to write the same Miss Manners-like statement a hundred times: "Good girls do not chew gum in class." Stout Mama wasn't chewing gum; she was chewing her lip, a habit she still falls into when she worries over an assignment. Even as a girl, Stout Mama thought that chewing gum looked bovine. She remembers telling that to her teacher. After the sentence about gum, she wrote "Good girls do not talk back" one hundred times.

And now she has to write a preface. Once again, she thinks she doesn't deserve this penance. She thinks suffering is the author's job.

Stout Mama knows she's been sitting at her table for hours, though the clock hands haven't moved. She looks down at the papers she's covered with writing and discovers it's all the same word: *preface*. She counts and finds she's written that a thousand times.

Now she feels like Scheherazade, condemned to come up with something sufficiently beguiling or lose her head at dawn. She begins to panic. She takes her lip between her teeth. She picks up her pen and writes; this time the word comes out *pre-face*. Stout Mama doesn't remember her birth, certainly does not recall being pre-face. She doesn't want to imagine such a state. But this is a nightmare and so, of course, she does, picturing a body topped by featureless dough, some monster in a grade-B horror flick like *The Blob*.

Stout Mama's fingers sweat around her pen. She extends it toward the dough where there should be eyes and makes two circles. But no lines appear beneath the pen; it must be out of ink. Stout Mama grabs a fresh one, tries some lips. They materialize, but before she can add a nose and eyes, the lips purse, drawing the dough beneath them into a jaw. Stout Mama watches, fascinated, as the jaw shifts into ruminative motions that she knows she's seen before. Somewhere in the distance a low mooing sound begins. The taste of last night's salad, coming back pureed now, rises in her throat. The beginning of a preface. The screaming wakes her up.

Stout Mama takes a big knife from the kitchen. Carefully, she slices all the prefaces from her books. When the recycling bin is full, she heats a cup of skim milk, spikes it with some Johnny Walker. She crawls back into the covers, feeling the whiskey warm her like the sun on her bikinied body strolling down the pier. She selects a book and dives into the story.

The Gym

In reality, Stout Mama is thin. But reality changes. It is like the mirror in the women's gym. From a distance, Stout Mama appears compact in the mirror, a little shorter than she feels, a little thick, as if a weight pressed her head and the lost height spread horizontally. As she walks toward the glass, her image changes fluidly, bulging, then slimming, finally settling into something small and athletic (a gentler name for stout). Stout Mama can never decide which distance from the mirror is the true one. Stout Mama can never decide what she means by truth. On good days, the slim distance matches her feeling and she accepts it. On bad days, the slim distance contradicts her feeling and she reaches for its reassurance, the way she reaches for the transparent hope in a glass of gin. On worse days, truth bulges. On the worst days of all, Stout Mama believes again that truth is out there, real and final, an image of her set forever in the eyes of the drunk on the street, the woman handing her a clean white towel—and she is lost outside it, can never be sure what they see.

Stout Mama asks a friend to the gym. She chooses
lockers at the end of the room so when they have
undressed they have to walk through all the stories
in the mirror to reach the showers. Stout Mama tries
to slow the walk down, but the friend moves quickly
and the bodies in the glass shift rapidly like lake
reflections in a storm.

Afterward they go for Bombay gin. When the drinks
arrive, the friend gets up to play the jukebox. Stout
Mama bends the lime around her glass rim. She feels
hopeful. Every image showed her thinner than her
friend. She looks up at the bar where two fat men in
leisure suits are drinking, one fatter than the other.
Stout Mama lifts her gin glass slowly, like opening a
book of elementary physics. She looked in the mirror, but she forgot to look first at her naked friend.

Mick Jagger's Birthday

*S*tout Mama has always loved Mick Jagger. She knows this is politically incorrect, but she has never taken the words of "Under My Thumb" seriously. She treats them like that album cover with faces of The Rolling Stones above push-up bras from Fredericks of Hollywood. The bras seem more threatening. Stout Mama is politically eclectic. She hasn't shaved her legs in years, but she paints her toenails.

Sometimes Stout Mama dreams she spends the night with Jagger. In her dreams, the sex is already over, and the two of them are talking about great literature. Once she dreamed she went into a large room where all the men who'd done her wrong were gathered. None of them knew she'd just spent the night with Mick Jagger. Stout Mama knew.

Today is Jagger's birthday. A local fern bar is holding a party, with concert films, continuous Rolling Stones tapes, and a cherry-flavored drink with large red cardboard lips pasted on the glass. Stout Mama has given up going to bars alone, but this time it seems almost like a duty. To herself, not Jagger. She remembers the concert in the Cleveland Stadium. She remembers camping out all night for tickets. She is sure that not making the effort to be a little silly on Mick Jagger's birthday would be a sign of age. Stout Mama is almost as old as Jagger.

No one in the bar is as old as Stout Mama. Everyone is in couples, and above the talk she can hardly hear the music. There is something overly memorial about the party, as if the children of the Veterans of Foreign Wars had gathered to watch the folks parade.

Stout Mama sees a good-looking man with several grey hairs. She sits down across from him. They trade three sentences. A younger man sits down beside the first. He runs a crab boat in Alaska. The grey one ran a newspaper in Fairbanks. They stop talking to Stout Mama.

Stout Mama talks to some boys who should have had their ID checked. They wear T-shirts with big lips and a plush tongue across their thin chests. Their hair is cut in flattops like her brother wore when she wore anklets. A television crew arrives and sets up near their table. They want to interview some experts on Mick Jagger. They pick the boys. Back home, Stout Mama gives her toenails a new color. Sitting on the edge of the bathtub, she waves her feet, waiting for the paint to dry. Her toes are neon blue with silver sparkles. She is thinking about great literature. It is long past midnight in England.

~~~~~~~~~~~~~~~~~~~~~~~~~~~~~~~~~~

Memory and the Freeway Queen

*L*ike a modern pony express rider, Stout Mama makes her living on the road, commuting from one college to another, for the part-time teaching jobs that, pieced together, keep her housed and clothed and fed. There are days, of course, when her thighs tell her she could do without being fed, but her stomach tells her otherwise. And so she drives, turning up the volume on the Volkswagen's tape deck, Bruce Springsteen wailing about '57 Chevys as she swings into the fast lane. In the days of '57 Chevys, her junior high friends called her the Queen of Rock and Roll; now she calls herself the Freeway Queen.

Some days, Stout Mama concentrates on driving. Other days, she's absentminded, putting the familiar four lanes on automatic pilot, planning her classes, writing a story in her head and holding it there till she can reach the typewriter. Stout Mama has a good memory for stories, and a terrible one for faces or names. She is constantly embarrassed on the street or at large parties by the people confidently addressing her, strangers she knows must be acquaintances, with identities her mind has not faithfully filed. If Stout Mama were more practical, she'd read some self-help book, like Dale Carnegie's *How to Win Friends and Influence People*, some guide offering tricks to correct a faulty memory. But Stout Mama grew up Catholic, and so does nothing but feel guilty, considering her defective memory a character flaw.

Today, the lanes are jammed: rush hour. The traffic creeps, then surges, then creeps again. The lane to the right of Stout Mama's stalled one suddenly surges, and a man in a passing car waves. A vigorous wave, the kind you give an old friend just reencountered. Stout Mama puts on her brightest "Of course, hello, I know you" smile, and waves too, plugging her memory into "search." He looks familiar, drives the sort of nondescript small car the people she knows habitually drive. But what's his name? She flagellates her character defect, hoping his lane will speed away, hoping he won't expect her to pull off at the next exit, to pull over and chat. Her own lane surges and she overtakes him. He's still waving, she smiles again. He pantomimes drinking a cup of coffee. She pulls a long, regretful face, pointing to her wrist, her nonexistent watch. Her lane leaves his behind.

By now, Stout Mama's memory banks have flagged each man she can remember that might fit his description, and rejected them all. Her freeway exit looms ahead like her final humiliation: two lanes curving down together into a stoplight. If he takes the same exit, if the light's red . . .

He does, and it is. Stout Mama smilingly rolls down her window, with all the grace of absentminded queens who've misplaced the name of some monarchical rival. The man leans out his window, handing her something white. His business card. "You're wonderful," he says. "Who are you?"

The Student

*T*he student is black haired and athletic. He has been a member of the college crew team for three years and his arms are well developed. His jaw is square, his nose straight, and his eyes blue. He dresses well in a Northwestern sort of way—natural fibers and a pair of unassuming cowboy boots. He could pose for an *Esquire* ad and later they could airbrush the acne. The student is a senior in premed, but without knowing the term he thinks of himself as a Renaissance man and takes electives in creative writing.

For weeks Stout Mama has been thinking about the student. This has never happened before. Once, for a day or two, she loved a student in her adult night class because he told her he'd been laid off from the railroad and anything to do with trains she finds romantic. Now bursts of giggles seize her in the middle of her lecture, and she has to stare toward the ceiling to make them stop. One day the class divided into groups, and she sat down next to the student to read the paper he was holding. She could feel her left shoe resting near his tooled boot, and nothing on the page made sense.

Stout Mama drives thirty miles to reach the college. She shares an office with a friend who has just been named department head. He has a brown velvet couch in the office, where the student sits on conference days. Stout Mama sits behind the desk, leaning back in the swivel chair, smoking. On the long round-trips she imagines plots, with cinematic variations. The student's face if she used the couch, her friend's face if he caught them. Changing the lock on the door. All the plots seem too worn out for even grocery store novels.

One afternoon, driving home from school, Stout Mama notices the days have gotten longer. She rolls down the window and it's spring. She lets the semi-trailers pass her, pulls over, and pulls off. Beside the road a tractor moves slowly up and down a field, and the earth rolls over, thawed. Stout Mama turns on the country and western station. She listens for a long time.

The next day she gives the class their last assignment. Write something honest. Put your real feelings into it. Talk about basic things like bars and broken hearts and cheated wives and trucks. At the end of the week, the students hand in their stories and the winter term is over. Stout Mama takes the papers home. The student's story is about a boy who is attracted to an older woman. He meets her in a bar every night for a week, but always leaves alone because he has a girlfriend in another city. On Friday night the girl comes for a visit. The boy does not want to go to the bar, but the girl insists, and finally he decides it will be better this way. The woman will see him with the girl and understand and everything will be over.

The woman is not in the bar. The boy drinks too much. Later, pulling out of the parking lot with his girlfriend, he sees the woman, but she's looking down and accidentally walks in front of his truck. Something goes wrong inside his brain and his foot won't hit the brake. He feels the impact of her body. People behind him are screaming then, and the girl is tearing at his arm, but he keeps on driving. He drives to the middle of a plowed field. He tells the girl they're safe.

Stout Mama drives to the Hallmark store. She buys a card shaped like a cowboy boot and puts the story inside. She mails it to the student.

Rats and S&M Black Leather

Stout Mama does not like cats. More precisely, Stout Mama does not like any pet that lives indoors. Having grown up on a farm, she believes that animals reside in pastures, chicken coops, and barns, perhaps the family's yard. They do not curl up on sofas or at the foot of beds.

Stout Mama has inherited a cat. She has rented a house, and the previous tenant has sworn that he'll be back for his cat, just as soon as he gets properly settled in his own new place. He has not left Stout Mama his phone number.

For a month, Stout Mama feeds the cat. Outdoors, of course—the place where cats are meant to live. The cat is not accustomed to this reasoning and hangs around the front door, jumps in through any open window. It is summer and muggy. Stout Mama feels like a prisoner in a private sauna. She can swelter or let in the cat. She swelters.

Stout Mama considers that even the patience of a

saint must falter after a month. She has always liked Saint Teresa, but Teresa suffered ecstasies, not cats. Stout Mama feels more like Saint Sebastian, lashed to a tree, putting up with a shower of arrows, endless as meows. She stops feeding the cat, assuming that like the collie in *Lassie Come Home*, it will sniff out its owner or, faithful only to its stomach, find a new one.

The cat stays. Some days the lawn is littered with feathers, but the cat remains hungry, and windows remain targets. Stout Mama opens one only when she's sitting watchfully beside it, closing it every time she leaves the room.

One night, Stout Mama is overly tired and forgets a window. The sound of thumps and scuffling wakes her—the signal, she's sure, of a cat invasion.

Stout Mama can't see well without her contact lenses, but she knows the cat is large and orange striped, and the thing rustling about the sofa is small and black. A rat.

The rat takes refuge in a stack of boxes. Stout Mama finds the mop, and then remembers her uncles telling stories about the barn, about the rats running up inside their overalls. Stout Mama has a horror of the rat's feet climbing on her bare ones. She goes back to her closet, pulls on her high-heeled boots, black leather up to the knee. In the boots and her short red flimsy nightgown, she feels she ought to wave a whip and not a mop. She stomps into the boxes. The rat leaps out and races toward the front door that she races to open—this time hoping for the cat, the born mouser taking on a bigger job, rewarding her for all those nights of dinners. There is no sign of the cat.

Until, of course, the morning, when it's back.

~~~~~~

Star Date

*W*hen the digital alarm beeps sharply into morning, Stout Mama hits the button for a little snooze, wakes again for the headlines that depress her and stock market reports that she can easily dream through, sure they're not important, sure that AT&T will go on overcharging her on late-night gossip, no matter what the latest quotes say. Stout Mama pulls the quilt closer, listening for the program called "Star Date," for the sixty seconds of cosmic news telling her what star will rise beside the moon tonight, what meteors would shower her if she would only sleep on beds of moss and pine needles, outside the lights of cities. Stout Mama waits for the voice of Joel Block, broadcasting from the observatory in Texas, waits for the way he says "I'm" in the final line: "And for the MacDonald Observatory, I'm Joel Block." His accent is not really southern, just a little prolonging of the vowel, a little softening. Stout Mama is in love with the way Joel Block says "I'm." Stout Mama is a fool for the sound of words. And so, Stout Mama is in love with Joel Block.

Stout Mama always goes to bed late. Once, she wakes at five, the middle of her own night, and there outside the window is a star so bright she knows it must really be a planet. She remembers what she's learned that week on "Star Date." She smiles hello to Venus. She thinks of that song by Frankie Avalon and of the black pompadour curls of the fifties. She goes back to sleep. In her dreams, she writes a letter to Joel Block, asking him the color of his hair, telling him she loves the way he curls his vowels.

Stout Mama leaves the country for a year. She goes to China, where the tones of sounds mark different words, and she finds herself in shops, asking for sugar, getting soup, because the syllables are the same but the tones are different. Stout Mama has a shortwave radio, but none of the waves are Texan, and for a year the voice of Joel Block is replaced by the Voice of America, like getting soup instead of sugar.

Stout Mama comes home. She sets her alarm. When it wakes her, she stretches lazily in her sheets, waiting to hear Venus rising in the gentle vowels of Joel Block's morning sign-off. But somehow the MacDonald Observatory has convinced him to take lessons in elocution. She hears a harsh long "I" in "I'm," a jarring emphasis. Professional. And empty as the city's neon skies.

Third World

Stout Mama has never owned a television. At school, she feels awkward and foolish in front of her students when the personnel from the audiovisual department desert her, and she has to try to insert a videotape in the VCR, an acronym she can't translate into words. She knows that CD stands for compact disc (or maybe disk), but the technology escapes her, like the spelling. Her own stereo is twelve years old and would be older, but some teenage thieves once broke into her home, riffling through her bureau drawers of cotton underwear and costume jewelry, looking for dope, disgusted at finding nothing. Out of spite, they stole her stereo, the old components like a World War II tank, purchased in her college days at a discount warehouse in Chicago.

Stout Mama does own a car, the same car she's always owned, the same Volkswagen beetle, with the paint that she calls Latin American red so faded now that everyone refers to her car as orange. Stout Mama corrects them. She hates orange. Her car also hates orange. Her car is patient but temperamental.

After fifteen years she has, as the mechanics say, thrown a rod. For some reason, this does not mean she needs a new rod, but a new engine. The logic of this defies Stout Mama. Stout Mama has thrown a great many fits, has thrown glasses and books, even thrown a pumpkin out a fifth-story window, hoping it would drop on the intended head. For her own fits, no one has suggested transplant surgery. She has cured them with another glass of wine, an evening of country and western lyrics, a day spent sleeping in past noon. Apparently, cars are more fragile. A thrown rod means a new heart. And so, Stout Mama's car beats down the highway to a rebuilt tune, her old soul patient and temperamental as ever.

Stout Mama knows her purchasing behavior is not American. She is not priming the economy. She has no desire to keep up with her neighbors, no desire even to know her neighbors' names, to be invited to a backyard barbecue, to chat over the daffodil bulbs in spring. When the five forks in her kitchen pile up dirty by the sink, Stout Mama washes her dishes by hand, avoiding the spatial arrangement tests of dish-washers. She loads her Volkswagen with laundry, sure that private washers and dryers—sitting idle for days at a time—are the offspring of a capitalist men-tality. She thinks the only drawback of communal machines is the drone of easy listening stations on the laundromat's loudspeakers.

Stout Mama likes to travel, living happily in places that her country names Third World. Inside her own nation, she feels Third World. Adrift in poetry and politics, she forgets to keep pace with technology, forgets that the little money she makes is supposed to be spent on goods and not good times. She drops further and further behind the changes in her country. Some days she surfaces, blinking like a groundhog perplexed by the shadow on the snow. Then she calls her travel agent, to talk tickets to the Third World.

Stout Mama has one modern vice. She likes her icebox, likes the simple ease of its constant presence, the bulb coming on reliably as a lighthouse beacon, shining on the milk and eggs and bread. But stocking the icebox creates a problem. No street markets in the States. She cannot ride her bike between the curbs of noisy vendors, only wheel an awkward cart down aisles, the shelves noisy with yellow signs announcing the day's special sales. Standing in front of the store's red coffee grinder, with its maze of levers and buttons, Stout Mama feels as if the bag of beans in her hand has transformed to a videocassette; over her shoulder she senses the eyes of competent shoppers, laughing like her students at the bewildered techno-peasant. Every week the supermarkets grow more complex, their functions less clear. They remodel into deli sections flanked by bulk food bins of herbs and grains, cookies and pretzels. Corners of them become cafés, with umbrellas over the tables, and espresso machines. Well-dressed young couples sit there, as if it were a sidewalk in Madrid. Well-dressed singles circle the aisles, with carts of diet foods and expensive wine, checking the contents of other carts at the register like résumés, exchanging glances and phone numbers. Stout

Mama consults her shopping list scrawled on the back of some junk mail envelope, no longer sure it's food that she should carry to the parking lot, no longer sure what parking lots are for. Singles' night at the supermarket seems like ladies' night in small-town bars, with the ultimate goal the same—some bargain in the backseat at a drive-in movie or in a cornfield.

Under the bright fluorescents, Stout Mama stands before the row of bulk diet soda, the plastic bottles tapping into giant vats below them, the signs naming flavors—strawberry and piña colada. She feels a kind of vertigo, and crumples her list in her palm. She walks out the automatic doors, past the new cars endlessly circling for parking places, and finds herself inside a Chinese restaurant in the same big shopping complex. On Third World time, the waiter strolls by. She knows she ought to ask for something slim and trendy, like sparkling water with a twist of lime, some low-salt gourmet crackers on the side. She orders Tsing Tao beer, heavy with a caloried malt, and dumplings, half a dozen, fat and doughy, fried in rhythms of some other century, as stubbornly out of step as hearts.

Dislocated Soldiers

Stout Mama has creative hearing. Having studied only Latin in high school, she has trouble understanding foreign tongues that living people actually speak. She gets the general sense of what's being said, but specific words can sometimes undergo strange transformations in her ears. Ordinarily, Stout Mama accepts this, checking her interpretation only when the words grow strange enough to cause doubt. One day, two friends discuss in French the situation of another woman—the particular personal oppressions she suffers inside the general oppression of being female in a patriarchal country inside a sexist world. "Did you say," asks Stout Mama, checking her hearing, "that the woman was *decapitée*, decapitated?"

"Oh no," the friends respond, a little horrified beneath their laughter. "We said the situation handicapped her, *handicapée*." Stout Mama feels her translation may be wrong linguistically, but in some deeper sense it's accurate.

Teaching in foreign countries, Stout Mama has seen the same creative hearing in her students. Often, texts are unavailable or too expensive. Or there is a text, but students don't bother to read it. They rely on lectures, on oral comprehension in a second or third nonmother tongue. Reading their exams, Stout Mama finds Ollie North taking a "bun rap," the Americans of the Great Depression losing their faith in "ragged individualism," South African blacks fighting for "universal sufferage"—something, Stout Mama observes, they already have. After World War I, the students maintain, there was a general sense of "disallusionment," a term Stout Mama thinks she ought to patent, like some French literary critic, like Jacques Derrida who's made his fame with words like "deconstructionism." Stout Mama thinks that "disallusionment" could be a tool for deconstructing writers overly fond of literary references. Imagine disallusioning *The Wasteland*.

Sometimes creative hearing is politically timely. Just after George Bush has sent thousands of troops to menace Iraq while he himself tees up for nine holes of manicured greens, a student writes that some Americans "preferred to spend their leisure time in playing gulf instead of going to church." Sometimes creative hearing reaches metaphysical heights. Discussing the love poems of John Donne, a student notes that "God is the fusion between a mistress and a loser."

Stout Mama does not "correct" the students. She understands creative hearing, how alternative ears can open up alternatives. She knows the power of such hearing even within a native tongue. She remembers how one night she "heard" a friend comment upon the pain of "dislocating your soldier." She thought of Dear John letters drifting into GI camps—those soldier boys the Motown voices wailed that they'd be true to. She felt her own lost loves like wayward ligaments, the ache of emptied sockets.

High School Sex

*T*his term, Stout Mama is filling in for a friend who teaches in a small-town high school. Her class is billed as creative writing in the schedule. In high school talk that means elective, aka nonserious time and an easy A. She has a back row of football players, a huddle of young blonde women teetering on stilt sling-back heels under a load of Revlon, two or three kids who drift in late after a bathroom cigarette. It's been balmy enough this week to open the windows to counteract the furnace the school continues to run full blast, and even the one intense poet in the front row hasn't heard a word she's said for two days.

Stout Mama lets the birds win. She tells the students to write whatever comes to mind, and leaves for a cup of tea. Teachers keep only coffee in the faculty pot, so she heads for the home ec room to heat some water in the microwave. Most days the home ec room is fun, more like recess than a class, with a few kids milling around in chocolate chips or pizza dough, the rest of them slouching on tables. Today she walks in on neat rows of seated students with their faces pulled long and chins disappearing into elbows of bored silence. The sex lecture.

Stout Mama remembers her own high school self, remembers sex lectures are ritual, annual as spring. Today, the female home ec teacher sits in back. The school has brought in a man with chalkboard diagrams and a voice as sexless as a computer. He's talking about the Whole Person. He has a diagram of circles within circles, and inside each circle is one piece of the Whole Person: the social piece, the intellectual piece, the physical health piece, the sex piece. He uses words like *component* that sound less racy than *piece*.

Stout Mama understands that the diagrams are simply prologue. Everybody knows he's here to talk about the sex piece; that's what he's paid for. But he's setting the scene, building a framework of dull cotton so the kids will be too half-asleep to snicker when he finally gets to the facts. That's what he's really paid for.

Stout Mama slips up the aisle like walking a mine field of suppressed snickers. Not the old-fashioned, fresh-faced embarrassed snicker. These kids live in the late twentieth century. Even small towns have cable movies, VCR rentals, and radio stations blasting hits by rap groups. They're laughing at this computer whose program probably reads once a week, Saturday nights after some wine, missionary position.

Stout Mama practices suppressing. She inserts her cup into the microwave and hides behind the chalkboard, waiting for technology to bring her water to a boil.

The prologue's finished. The man announces tonelessly that what he's about to say is simply the facts of it, encyclopedic, and must not be taken as advocating anything. He's ready for the organs. "Let's start with the female," he suggests.

Sure. They always start there. Women and children overboard first. Warm up the water before the men get in. Stout Mama grabs her boiling cup and heads for the door. The man has chalked up ovaries and fallopian tubes, and now he's drawing what he refers to as the vaginal canal. Stout Mama wonders briefly if this is a class in obstetrics. "Also," states the lecturer, "we have the female external genitals." He doesn't draw them.

Stout Mama closes the door and walks back to class, surprising her students, who quickly stub their cigarettes into butts tossed out the window. They've written something in their collective heads: a story about a male rock star who punched a C&W fan senseless in a redneck bar and always sang about sex.

"Sex," Stout Mama says, and mentions where she's been. Her students are seniors; the school believes in preventive maintenance, so they heard the ritual last year. The same man. In Stout Mama's class, students feel free not only to snicker, but also to groan. They groan.

"Well, then you know the one I mean," she grins, "the man that draws the ovaries and the fallopian tubes and the vaginal canal and gives up when he gets to the good stuff." The football faces in the back row turn away from the window for the first time this week. She could stick a hatpin in the blondes now and not a one would blink.

Stout Mama turns to the chalkboard. "Clitoris," she says. "It's something like character motivation or a conflict in the plot. Something you should know about."

They listen past the bell.

Stout Mama's Dreams— Number 50

*T*he basketball game has just ended in the high school gym, but there's terrible rivalry between the teams, something as ancient as adolescence and Greek city states, something as modern as nationalism in the regions of the former Soviet Union. Boys who don't know each other. And are therefore afraid. And are slamming each other and everything movable like chairs against the walls. Stout Mama's caught in the crowd that spills out into the lobby but can't find its way past the doors. In the shapeless mill of arms and legs, one teenage boy takes form. "I know the cop's have spotted me before, dealing dope," he says, "and I want you to turn me in. I want the safety of their escort now, out of this gym."

Cemeteries in Roslyn

Most small towns build their graveyards at the edge where Main Street turns back into highway, the first or last thing you see, passing through. But this one's deeper, on a side road off a side street. Rain has turned the road to quicksand, sucking at Stout Mama's heels. She remembers childhood tales about the dead reaching out to haul the living under. Still, the rain seems right for exploring graveyards. She likes a weather that's symbolic, even when the symbolism is clichéd.

Roslyn's an old coal-mining town, more people buried here than living. Some civic pride has put up signs, explaining what Stout Mama sees. She'd recognize the oldest section anyway, by the marble lambs with broken necks and the headstones toppled into forests of ferns. But the sign has more to tell her than just dates: "Here lie the remains of men killed in the mines and children dead from epidemics." Apparently no women died.

Stout Mama thinks they lived, and moved away. She looks at the good tall stone that Susan Weatherly

chose for her husband Jacob, big enough to hold a
love poem, an anomaly in this field of "gone but not
forgotten" inscriptions. She imagines the women
outliving the men, putting their own stone in early
with the birth date waiting for the death date to be
carved. Susan left only her name above the poem.
Stout Mama wonders whether Susan wrote it. She
wonders what women think, dying maybe half a
world away from where they've left their birth date
on a stone, deciding which husband to lie beside.

Does the last one always win by being last? Did any
woman ever have her bones shipped back to rest
beside a husband she liked better or beside a lover?
Did some stay rooted in a town because a grave
waited? Where male and female names line up
along a plot, how many times has she been wrong to
call them brother, sister, cousin? It could be wife and
husband, wife and husband, an endless string of
replacements linked like a child's paper chain.

Men died in the mines. Women died in childbirth.
Some got replaced. The town got smaller, and the
graves climbed further up the hill. Stout Mama pictures Susan climbing a stagecoach step, her best
black packed forever in a trunk. The morning she
left, it must have rained like this, with the sun on the
hills behind the drops like a face behind a rhinestone
veil. Stout Mama thinks that wherever Susan's
buried, she's alone.

Jacob was English. He's buried in the oldest section
where the bones of different nationalities lie mixed
together. Later the lodges formed and split the dead

up, the Slavs in the Doctor Starkovich Lodge, the
Italians naming their group exotically—*Cacciatore
d'Africa*, Hunter of Africa—the Eagles fencing themselves off from everybody with an accent. A lodge
was like insurance, money for accidents or death.
The matchbook in Stout Mama's pocket advertises
some insurance company's death benefits. She's been
picking those matchbooks up for weeks in supermarkets when she buys cigarettes. Some days she
thinks it's a plot, but she can't really credit supermarkets with a sense of symbols, even when the
symbolism is that clichéd.

A lodge was more than symbols—a human circle
drawn against hard winters and weak timbers in the
mines. Someplace to drink and dance and eat pie.
Someone to speak the language you felt at home in
and carve it on your gravestone.

Stout Mama notes how lodges keep their separate
natures even in death—the Italians on a shady curve
of hill, graves set chaotically between the ferns and
vines; the Slavs on a clear slope, in perfect rows
facing east, energetic for the first light. In the small
porcelain photos on their stones, the Slavs don't
smile. Stout Mama can't imagine them with anything as frivolous as poems or harps, only rolling
up the sleeves on stolid arms to chop wood, knead
a mass of dough to good dark heavy bread.

In Roslyn, maybe only Susan Weatherly wrote
poems. Maybe only Jacob read them. What could
she do when he died but carve them on his stone,
yearning "for the touch of a vanished hand, / and

the sound of a voice that is still." The morning that she stepped into the stagecoach, the east was hills of ponderosa pines breaking up the clouds, behind them, sun and open country brushed with sage.

Stout Mama follows Susan, aiming her car toward the highway. A crow just skims the hood, and the flag above the military graves snaps suddenly in the wind, jerking her back to thoughts of ghosts. She laughs them off. The war's the only thing that's truly dead here. Even the dying town has new paint on the houses, makeshift storm windows coming off for May, and mended fences where the dog broke out last week.

Elk

They make a grace of browns, blend with the hills behind the reservation feeding grounds. Strange composite animals, almost camel-like, but moving as lightly as deer, their shaggy necks shading off into short-furred rumps and bellies.

Stout Mama is admiring the elk, pressing her nose against the wire mesh fence around the feeding ground where the wildlife rangers have strewn hay. Stout Mama's friend, a painter with a growing reputation for her politicized renderings of local scenes, is sketching. A big sign to the left of the hay says the reservation was established by federal order in 1950. It says the elk are harvested on a periodic schedule. It asks the "sportsmen" to please check in with ranger headquarters. Stout Mama's friend has sketched the sign; now she's working on the elk that's scratching its rump against it.

Two vans packed with men drive up, one with a big Gospel Sing poster on the side, the other with Jesus painted backwards on the front, so drivers can read

it in their rearview mirrors. Stout Mama and her
friend take refuge in their own car. The men mill
about for ten minutes, trying to feed the elk potato
chips and Cokes. The elk beside the sign stops
scratching, joins the herd that's filing slowly toward
the hills. The men file back inside their vans. As they
leave, a tiny beat-up car pulls in, some sort of gener-
ic U.S. compact. A man with a wheelbarrow-sized
stomach climbs out the small door, unfolding
mounds of flesh, a giant camera hanging from his
neck, a camera belt loaded with film cartridges holding up his pants. A camper with a tall CB antenna
parks beside him, and his pals jump out. The three
of them talk elk.

"They're out there. There's horns out there. But
they're keepin' away from us."

The stomach lifts the camera. Stout Mama wonders
if he's taking pictures of the ones he wants to harvest
the next time the periodic schedule rolls around.

The other two men laugh, whistle loudly, and hoot.
The elk shy and scatter up the hills.

"They're up there," the stomach says. And then a
long pause. "But we're buggin' 'em."

Stout Mama glances at her friend, who rolls her
eyes. "A philosophic moment for him," she says and
starts the engine, letting their noisy takeoff roar like
poorly choked-back laughter.

Learning to Be a Father

*S*tout Mama lives in a rainy city and grows easily tired of rain. She likes to cross the mountains that divide her state, rising like the clouds that drop their burden of water on the west side, passing into the eastern sunlit desert. But this presents a problem. Stout Mama can drive uphill, but on the steep downgrades hysteria grips her, a phobia that's come upon her slowly. She remembers that years ago she drove Pikes Peak alone, steering calmly up and down its washed-out red dirt switchbacks. Now her palms sweat even on the climb, like a preview of the trip back, the ascents reversed and lined with road signs featuring nose-down silhouettes of semitrailers, the numbers below them listing the diagonal miles of terror left to navigate.

Luckily, Stout Mama's friends have different phobias. She can curl up in their backseats, watching the light on pine boughs shift from grey to sun. But some friends drive too fast and the countryside blurs, passing too quickly for Stout Mama to absorb. This is a price of phobias.

Stout Mama also likes snow, and the snow is also in the mountains. She wants to spend a few days skiing. Cross-country, of course—in gentle valleys. But the friends that she depends on as chauffeurs are busy. This is another price of phobias. Sometimes it's too much to pay. And so today Stout Mama feels like a cognitive behaviorist, talking back to herself while she loads skis onto her Volkswagen, telling herself one fear is succeeded by another, a ripple effect she has to break before its concentric circles lock her inside her own front door.

In bad driving stretches, Stout Mama has a habit of talking to her car, but on this trip she thinks the car's attention will be elsewhere, the old gears busy hanging on to the winter roads. She looks for conversation substitutes to keep her mind off fear. She loads the tape deck with Patsy Cline and Merle Haggard; she packs her teddy bear, setting him upright in the passenger's seat, the red ribbon around his neck incongruous below his fierce stuffed face. She spent hours in department stores looking for a face like that, in the days when the latest anger-release therapies recommended punching bears. The search itself was therapeutic; she realized that all her life she'd been looking for a tough bear, one she could punch and later hug in bed. Once she found the bear, she never hit him.

Snow packs the mountain pass, the road dropping into indefinite whiteness. It's all Stout Mama can do not to lie down beside the highway, say she can't go on. But talking to the bear helps. And there's a village with a nice motel just halfway down the eastern descent. Stout Mama props the bear on the bed, but when the maid comes in, she feels embarrassed, has to explain her phobia to justify the presence of the bear. The maid nods, sympathetic, and admits she has lived here five years and didn't drive the pass herself until last winter. She waxes chatty. She says her husband has recently allowed her to have this job, but now she can't decide between continuing to work or enrolling in the college in the next town. "What would you study?" Stout Mama asks. "Psychology," the maid replies. Stout Mama checks, but the maid isn't smiling, not looking at the bear.

Stout Mama skis. She takes a turn she thinks will make a gentle round-trip loop, but she ends up on a high ridge, miles from her car, the sunset glowing rose across the snow. There's a long descent to the road. There are big dogs on the dark road, and happily, two men in a truck that offer her and the skis a lift on the last stretch to her car. For only a few hundred dollars, Stout Mama muses, she could have done a tourist package to Hawaii.

But the snow is crisp, the maid therapeutic, and the food authentically Bavarian in the restaurants in this fake Bavarian village. The day Stout Mama has to leave, she waves the maid a wistful farewell, thinking maybe she should make a deal, change sheets in return for room and board while the maid studies Freud. She considers this alternative more seriously when the blizzard hits, the fist-sized flakes slamming her windshield as she nears the summit of the pass. The plows have shoved small walls of snow along the road's edge, which is lined with truckers wrapping their tires in giant chains.

Stout Mama has chains in her trunk, but she's never had to use them. In her Midwest childhood, it was always her father who got out and cursed and put on the chains. Now Stout Mama learns that teddy bears are useless in the task of fastening chains, that phobias are less difficult to wrestle with than cold steel links. She squats awkwardly above the snow, tugging. Over and over she feels she's almost got it, starts the engine, backs into the last weave of chain. Over and over, but the links still won't close around her tires. Defeated, she climbs inside her car, proposing to camp there till the blizzard is finished, hoping the Volkswagen won't be buried by the spray from snowplows. She leans her head against the bear's. Suddenly an image of her father flashes, like a photo from an old textbook, an image of him lying down in the snow, his fingers red and bare and frozen, to get that last sheer fraction of leverage on unwieldy steel. Stout Mama gives up the luxury of squatting and lies down, like a Midwest child creating angel patterns, surrendering to the white wet cold. The links close up around her tires the way her father's knuckles closed around her small ones. They grip the downgrades home.

Super Bowl Eagles

It is the time of year to make the pilgrimage to see the eagles, multitudes of them wintering in the mountains northeast of Stout Mama's city, feeding on the spawned-out carcasses of chum and coho salmon, stripping them to fanged skeletons on the river bank.

Stout Mama and her friends are Audubons. They make the pilgrimage as faithfully as old Muslims climbing in their veils and white robes onto Mecca-headed planes. Stout Mama and her friends dig out down jackets and binoculars. They gas up at the local station and head in search of gods of cold and long black soaring feathers.

The road winds through a valley with a tiny white church at one end, red farm roofs at the other, and shreds of fog swirling above the snow. Just where the real climb begins, where the road turns at a bridge with dizzy views between the open chain-work metal of its flooring, there is the river—the place to stop for eagles. Today, the pine branches are studded with big sleek-feathered bodies and the white heads known as bald. The river banks are studded with tourists.

Not all the tourists have binoculars. Not all the tourists are Audubons. Not all the tourists know the rules and proper awe of pilgrimage. Instinctively, Stout Mama and her friends dislike one couple, the wife telling the husband, "Well, I've seen ten of them now," and going on counting, as if keeping score was all that mattered. The Audubons raise their eyebrows and start packing up binoculars, a signal that it's time to leave.

Stout Mama and her friends are Audubons, but not purists. They never rise at dawn to check for birds. What rites they undertake, they give a personal shape to. For them, a pilgrimage includes a ritual drink imbibed in the proper setting. After eagles in winter, they like Irish coffees, without sugar, in some small-town bar along the route home, the kind of place where tough middle-aged women with pack-a-day rasps to their laughter tend the bar, trading jokes and gossip with the men in ball caps and plaid shirts. A place with country and western on the jukebox, the steady crack of pool balls.

As Audubons, Stout Mama and her friends have seasonal schedules governed by migration patterns, not by *TV Guide*. But just inside the bar, the big-screen television roar alerts them: Super Bowl Sunday, a mainstream ritual they've forgotten, crowding out their own small rites. Drifting from one rejected tavern to another, every small-town

42

sanctuary occupied by touchdowns, they feel like the righteous driven into exile, and righteously proud of what society would call their heretical crimes. They're sure that if the FBI should ever pick them up, their files would say they never watched a Bowl game, never even knew the teams' names.

Revenge on Harleys

A man who rides a Harley shouldn't lie to his lover. Too many ways to wreak revenge upon the Harley. Sugar in the gas tank, a shower of eggs congealing on the paint under an oven of sun, a honed kitchen knife filleting the tires. For a week, Stout Mama has been paraphrasing Elizabeth Barrett Browning: "How do I get back at thee? Let me count the ways."

Stout Mama has been known to act precipitously, but usually she mulls things over. The longer she mulls, the less dramatic her revenge becomes. By the end of the week, she has scaled her motorcycle vengeance down to bubble gum.

Stout Mama imagines the Harley garlanded with pink, sticky strands. She pictures thick blobs on the seat waiting in the dark street for her unsuspecting lover to sit down, the gummed handlebars waiting to be grasped by his hands in expensive leather gloves. Stout Mama suffers uncontrollable fits of laughter every time this image floats before her eyes.

The laughter bubble gums her broken heart. Mended, she heads for the store, buys two hard-shelled globes of gum, like overgrown marbles, one red as Mars, one swirled with blue and white the way Venus looks in satellite photos.

Stout Mama wants to see her lover's face once he is pasted to his Harley. She plans to attend the weekly gathering of artists at a local café where her lover is a regular. She'll arrive late, so the motorcycle will be parked outside already, easily bubble gummed. Then she'll join the gathering, leaving when the others do, which is always late at night and en masse. In the mirror, she practices wide-eyed innocence, trusting the exclamations of the crowd to cover any snorts of laughter she can't choke back.

Stout Mama is fashionably late for the gathering, but finds her lover is even more fashionable. When he does arrive, there is one clap of thunder on what till then has been a cloudless evening. Stout Mama tells herself that omens are the stuff of superstition and grade-B horror films, useful for the box office, but nothing else. She slips outside, stuffing the marbles of gum in her mouth. There's the Harley by the doorstep, but other people keep arriving. Stout Mama pretends to read the posters on the wall, turning her jaws away from sight, interrupting her chewing. The bubble gum begins to taste like moldy plastic. And just when the street empties, rain falls, a gentle shower, but enough to make the bike too slippery for the gum to stick. The strands on the handle-bars dangle and turn hard; the wads on the seat slide.

Stout Mama gives up on the pink lumps like a child frustrated by modeling clay. She walks half a block down the street and looks up into cloudless sky. The rain has stopped. Just some Harley guardian angel at the faucet, watering down the taste of sweet revenge.

The Spirit Trap

Stout Mama does not believe in god. Too superstitious, too beardedly judgmental, too male. Too
easily a right-wing cause, and a cause for wars. As a
teacher of writing, Stout Mama knows that an argu-
ment based on the "appeal to authority" is a weak
one. To illustrate this with her students, she reminds
them of how they felt when they asked their mothers why they must do something they didn't want to
do and their mothers replied, "Because I say so."

Because the world seems so suffused with the reli-
gious lately, Stout Mama sometimes thinks about
religions. She wonders why no new ones have been
born. Oh, there have been phenomena like the
Reverend Moon, but nothing that's caught on in a
big way. Stout Mama considers the stories of men
upon which religions have based themselves.
Haven't there been such leaders in the last one thousand years or so? What about Ho Chih Minh or Che
Guevara—men Stout Mama found more charismatic
than Christ or Mohammed. And more good looking.
She pictures the skinny Christs on crucifixes in the

bedrooms of her childhood, the broad flat footprint of the Prophet she saw encased in bronze in a Turkish museum. Perhaps her choices of male leaders were too down-to-earth, like her attitudes toward them. Perhaps the days of credulous belief in things like multiplying loaves and fishes are over, and people are just clinging to the status quo. That would explain the recent worldwide rise of fundamentalisms. Humans hang on stubbornly to outworn habits. As a smoker, Stout Mama knows.

Stout Mama prefers talismans. She thinks if you're going to be superstitious, you might as well be direct about it. She chooses hers eclectically: a silver hand of Fatimah, amber prayer beads, a papyrus painting of the goddess Nut, a stuffed cotton fish, a blue glass marble with an iris and pupil—things to protect one from the evil eye. She likes the word the French use for such talismans: *prophylactiques*. She thinks of cosmic sleights of hand and earthly ruses, of condom manufacturers and Trojan horses. Sometimes she makes her own additions to the prophylactic world. When a friend gives her a small sequined woman as a Christmas tree ornament, a stuffed cloth figure in the aesthetics of the Venus of Willendorf, Stout Mama hangs it above her desk, a prophylactic against big thighs.

Stout Mama has been reading about Tibet. In the days of sixties' mysticism, she read *The Tibetan Book of the Dead*, rites for passing over. Now, in the nineties, Stout Mama is more interested in rites for peace of mind in the here and now. Following the instructions in her Tibetan books, she has constructed a spirit trap, weaving the skull of a goat (begged from the local butcher) with threads interlaced in spirit-trapping patterns. Stout Mama hangs it in her kitchen. The books say that when she has caught a demon, she should set fire to the trap. They do not say how to recognize trapped demons. Stout Mama sleeps uneasily, getting up sometimes at 4:00 A.M., insomniac's hour, to check the trap. How will she know when she's caught a demon? Or demons? How many angels on the head of a pin? How many soldiers in a prophylactic horse?

Hot Flushes

*S*tout Mama's grip on reality has always been tenuous, and now she's lost even the last fingernail hold. This hasn't happened overnight. For the last two months, she's been feeling the ground give way beneath her, like a slow-motion rock slide, her fingers less and less able or willing to take the strain of clinging to the last bit of cliff.

It began with forgetting things, or rather with the inability to remember them. She'd find herself striding purposefully into the kitchen only to falter when she arrived, standing between the icebox and the cupboards, asking herself why she'd come there, and drawing a blank.

Then she found she could concentrate on those blanks but on nothing else. Her mind wandered from the lines of print her eyes kept tracing till the rustle of the page turning under her hand snapped her back to attention, but the story's plot seemed alien, some crucial connection she'd missed. She shifted in her work chair as constantly as a kindergartner at her first desk. She played with her hair. She played with the phone cord during conversations, embarrassed when her friends asked, "Well, what do you think of that?" and she had no idea what they'd been talking about.

She couldn't sleep. She tried hot milk, tried whiskey, counted sheep, goats, pink elephants. She swung between depressed and more depressed. One morning when she went downstairs to check the mail, she found her box was empty, and she nearly went back to bed.

That was the first month.

Stout Mama's mind has always been more flighty than her body, but in the second month, her body let its cliff-hold slip. It bloated like a force-fed goose in the last days before Christmas dinner. Buttons on her skirts snapped suddenly when she sneezed. Her fat increased its productivity index, and the new flesh wasn't stout, but soft and spongy with a crepey fold. She felt cold, then hot—really hot: the sudden rush of a steaming cup of tea drunk under an equatorial noon sun in 100 percent humidity. But the weather was inside, the sun's rays pouring from her blood. She changed the damp sheets. She crawled back into bed in fresh pyjamas, leaving the blankets on the floor. She was cold. She hauled the blankets back.

Stout Mama has always liked to play poker. She likes to bluff, to up the ante, pretending she holds a full house or a straight flush when she has only one pair. She has three women friends who, like her, have eschewed the contractual solemnities of bridge for the joker's wild of poker, bluffing while the cigarettes burn in the ashtrays, the bottle of Jim Beam grows steadily emptier. Tonight they've gathered for a game, and Stout Mama notices that one woman keeps taking off her jacket, then putting it on. When the moment arrives to show their hands, the woman lays her cards down, slyly grinning. "I've got a hot flush," she announces. "Can you beat that?"

Stout Mama's friends are older than Stout Mama. They all start laughing, with a wise, knowing ring to the sound. Stout Mama thinks the plot's turned alien once again, some crucial thread lost. "What's happening?" she asks. And learns the name for cliffs to get a mid-life grip on. *Menopause*.

The Recalcitrant Screw

*S*tout Mama thought she'd found a playmate. A nice, intelligent, good-looking, intense young man. Maybe overly intense—but Stout Mama has been training herself to be tolerant, not overly picky. A man significantly younger than Stout Mama but tiring significantly sooner than she does. "You're very acrobatic," he says, and rubs the circles under his eyes, with a dubious grin. "Men hit their peak of sexual prowess at eighteen, and women in their forties. It's not fair," he says. Stout Mama thinks it's just a likely excuse, but she is training herself to be tolerant. The man has trained his dog to bark ferociously whenever she hears the word *Republicans*. Stout Mama thinks a man with politics like that is worth some tolerance.

But it is not easy. He likes to rise at 5:00 or 6:00 A.M. to write and to be silent and distant. Stout Mama thinks that silence is imperative in the morning. She never answers the phone before 9:00 or 10:00 A.M. But distance is another matter. She would like a small hug when he rises, a delicate kiss on the forehead, not enough to wake her, but enough to say he's glad she's there. He considers her request a form of pressure. Under pressure he grows silent and distant, what Stout Mama calls the worst form of mean and evil. She has always said she likes a mean man who is nice to her. This combination has been difficult to find.

But Stout Mama is training herself to be patient. She makes a dinner date with her playmate, steering him gently through his frets about his busy schedule, assuring him that she'll go easy so he won't be too tired to write in tomorrow's predawn. She thinks sometimes he approaches an evening of pleasure like a condemned man lifting the silver dinner lid on his last meal. She hangs up the phone, resisting the desire to slam the receiver, and goes out to the back driveway to work on her Volkswagen, to replace the broken handle that rolls the driver's window up and down. The old screw that has held the handle in place for twenty years refuses to budge, no matter how hard she turns the screwdriver, no matter how much graphite she pumps around the screw to ease its catatonic hold. After forty minutes of patience, Stout Mama slams her tools down on the driveway, first wishing for a man with a truck, the sort of man that always has a fresh can of WD-40 to lubricate a bolt, then disgusted with herself for entertaining such a stereotypically helpless wish. She goes inside to call her playmate, to ask him to stop by the hardware store on his way to her house. But the light on her answering machine is blinking with some neurotically distant message from her playmate, canceling their date.

Stout Mama checks the yellow pages for a reliable source of WD-40. She looks under *B* for Bars, subheading, Country and Western. She rats her hair into the tolerance of Tammy Wynette. She gives up on recalcitrant screws.

Reasons for Travel

At eighty-five, Stout Mama plans to give up diets. She plans to move to Mexico, to Zihuatanejo where she'll drink Negra Modelo and eat frijoles thick with salsa till she blossoms lush and blowsy as the pink hibiscus, wrapped like a tamale in her sun-drenched skin. She'll buy *pan dulce* for the dawn beach, the pastel sugar on the buns melting against her lips, the yellow butterflies massing above the waves. She'll sway naked and heavy in her midnight hammock, with the fingers of the sultry breeze slipping between the weave, and the palm leaves dark against the stars. Finally giving in to appetite will keep her young, a kind of sensual second childhood. Stout Mama likes the way Latinos prefer a woman with flesh; she plans to give them plenty of it, to be amply erotic.

But today Stout Mama is less than halfway to that freedom, and still obsessed with slender romance. She sits at her blue kitchen table, turning the pages of the *World Atlas*, spoon half-buried in a wedge of grapefruit. She hasn't given up on diets, only on the local men. And disappointment is bad for Stout Mama, drives her into late-night binges on double-cream Brie and French bread. Just last week she tipped the gym scales past her limit. She'd like an income in three figures, but not a weight. She thinks she's too short to be rich. All the women from the wealthy class seem born with long bones. She knows she's too short to happily bank much weight.

This morning, travel seems the most effective diet. And so Stout Mama turns the pages of the atlas, flipping the switch on her radio for background rhythm. The jazz station is playing "A Night in Tunisia," one of Stout Mama's old favorites, with an electric violin leading the tune's exotic, energetic strains. She scats along, one of the few songs she can match the melody of, maybe because its own harmonies are so dissonant. She remembers Paul Klee painted watercolors of Tunisia, a delicate riot of pastel shapes suspended in a pale gold wash of sands. The song and watercolors are all she knows about Tunisia. Stout Mama rarely makes a rational decision, only choices improvised romantically. She dials her travel agent.

Stout Mama believes in omens, what her more sophisticated friends call Jungian synchronicity. One midnight, a week after she has bought her ticket for Tunisia, she runs out of wine. She heads for the nearest 7-11. The magazine rack stands beside the cooler and a headline on a travel journal catches her eye—"Madam, Your Camel Is Here"—an article about Tunisia. She knows coincidence like this must mean some cosmic *Good Housekeeping* Seal on her decision. She buys the journal.

Settled in her big mauve chair, with her short legs
curled up and her thighs tucked out of sight beneath
her thick robe, Stout Mama sips her wine and begins
the article. She learns that she'll be traveling during
Ramadan, when Muslims drink no alcohol and fast
from dawn to dusk. No cigarettes and no sex until
the sun's eye closes, round and red behind the day's
last shimmering mirages on the sands. No problem.
It wasn't a song called "A Day in Tunisia" that
prompted her decision. She reads on. She learns that
the Arabic word for *camel* has nineteen other mean-
ings as well, including *huge mountain, bachelor,*
shroud, black stallion, lonely place, opinion, suspicion,
horse's bit, and *imaginative man.* She admires the flexi-
bility of Arabic and its precision, summing up so
many attributes of her former lovers in one word.
But Stout Mama begins to worry; if the language has
such synchronicity with her experience, will
Tunisian men be copies of the men she's known,
reflecting all her past romantic disappointments in
exact detail—the way mirages in the desert fake the
shapes of distant oases and leave you thirsty? She
takes comfort in her ignorance of the language—in
Arabic the words for *faithful* and *faithless* will be
indistinguishable to her.

The travel writer notes that, traditionally, Arab
women leave their houses only when veiled, the
cloth draped so that not even one eye is exposed,
and this protects their honor. An old proverb cautions the men: "Do not contribute to opening the eye
of a young girl if you do not want to find it impossi-
ble to close it." Such wisdom reassures Stout Mama.
She will trust the men to follow its advice. To call

58

herself a young girl might be stretching even languages as accommodating in their definitions as Arabic seems. But still her eyes are as innocent as all the endlessly fresh truths in proverbs. She has never blinked at love.

~~~~~~

Ma's Cow

*S*tout Mama knows she talks funny. Growing up
in Illinois, in a town whose name rhymed with
Andy Griffith's television Mayberry, she hated the
accent, the broad nasal *a*, and she erased it from her
vocal cords: she read a great many British novels;
she tried to do without the subtitles in French films;
she sang along with Diana Ross and The Supremes.
Somehow, these accents blended strangely in the
rhythms of her voice. When she hears herself on
tape, she knows she sounds like a twelve-year-old
girl from Alabama who's just returned from a grand
tour of Europe with her rich aunt.

Sometimes Stout Mama teaches briefly in small rural
towns. The students tell her she talks funny and ask
her where she's from. Stout Mama makes them
guess. Never having traveled more than twenty
miles from their own Main Streets, the students have
no reference points for accents, but a fine exotic
sense of possibilities. Randomly, they guess
Zimbabwe, Argentina, or Tunisia—names they've
seen on the big maps that pull down from rollers

above the chalkboard, names Stout Mama also finds exotic. In some larger sense of truth, the students are correct. Stout Mama really does believe her voice comes from such places. How disappointing then to have to give the students facts, to admit to birth in Illinois.

Stout Mama has a friend from England. He is more confident in his opinions than her students; he knows she just talks funny, like anybody from the States, where the different accents simply add up to the same conclusion: wrong. He has a sense of humor. He corrects her English constantly, constantly joking as he does it. Stout Mama has a sense of humor too, a little feistier than his—a little street smarts, a little rural wit. One day, while discussing the latest Eastern European politics, Stout Mama makes a reference to Moscow. For a moment, her English friend looks puzzled, and then he laughs. "You mean *Moss-coe,*" he says, correcting her pronunciation once again.

"No," Stout Mama says, "I mean *Moscow,* that name like an old woman calling her Hereford home from the pasture—*Ma's cow.*"

The Language of Cures

*N*ormally, Stout Mama loves language—the shades of meaning, the sounds and rhythms of the words themselves. She likes to play with words the way children just learning to speak play, repeating them simply for the joy of feeling them on her tongue. But lately, Stout Mama's found a language that she hates: medical terminology. She has been reading books on what used to be called "The Change." The content of the books is bad enough, inconclusive information on the various effects of hormones, dire predictions that without those hormones her bones will turn brittle—she'll break a hip or end up as stooped as the hunchback of Notre Dame. The language of the books is worse—ugly polysyllabic terms she can hardly twist her lips around: *estropipate, medroxyprogesterone acetate, norethindrone.* She's been trying out those words in tablet form and found they're just as ugly in her body as on the page. They have a way of making her feel fragile, of arriving as suddenly as a train from hell with a freight load of depression, sending her to bed for the rest of the day. Stout Mama thinks that if this continues, she won't live long enough to resemble Quasimodo; she'll have driven her Volkswagen off some bridge high enough to break even the strongest femurs and fibulas.

Stout Mama has a friend who studies naturopathy. She loans Stout Mama a book on naturopathic cures, a tome so thick and heavy Stout Mama considers never opening it, simply using it for weight-lifting exercises to build up her bones. Still, one night she turns to the section on osteoporosis. Not a good start, she muses, noting the chapter's medical title, the mass of terminology following it. She pages to the chapter's end where botanical medicines are listed. "Unicorn root," she reads. "Fennel . . . black cohosh . . . blessed thistle." She tries the words out loud, and then again and again till they become a little mantra, a Mother Nature's lullaby.

Stout Mama drops her bottles of medical terminology in the garbage. She heads for the poetics of the health food store.

~~~~~~

Big Time Wrestling

*T*hree nights a week, Stout Mama puts on a black skirt, white blouse, and oversized red blazer and moonlights as an usher at the local coliseum. She likes being allowed backstage with the clowns and sword swallowers, smoking on the back steps with the roadies that drive the rock stars' equipment vans. She likes seeing shows she'd never have paid money for—The Ice Follies and Neil Diamond concerts, Billy Graham and big time wrestling.

Lately, Stout Mama has been obsessed by wrestling, by the crowd that attends each match as faithfully as Christians observing Sunday, by the hocus-pocus of the promoters and the ethos of the wrestlers— especially the ones named bad guys. Her fascination is not with the bad guys themselves, but with how they've acquired that label. Sometimes, they've simply chosen images that milk the crowd's stereotyped reactions. So there's a bad guy Pole and a bad guy A-rab, wrestlers without names, only ethnicities. Where the label rests upon behavior, events can change a wrestler's status. Buddy Latona, for example, was a bad guy till Billie Rose broke his arm. Billie Rose is the quintessential bad guy, a fat, bleached blonde, a red-lipped punk, with puffy cheeks and eyes screwed in a spiteful squint against the injustice that gave him a baby face. He reminds Stout Mama of boys she knew in high school.

In the sixties when she turned sixteen, the Billie Roses drove souped-up Chevys with the rear ends jacked to forty-five degree angles over semitrailer tires and loud pipes blasting out of the tail. The Billie Roses packed themselves six in a car at the local drive-in, their windows strapped to trays of chocolate malts, hamburgers in orange cellophane wraps with french fries greasing the edges. They taunted the cars of couples, fanned the carhop's ass when they wheeled out. Here we are, their tires said, laying rubber on this strip of asphalt. And now, on this strip of wooden platform, squinting and squeezed into their tight red wrestling trunks—bad guys.

The bad guys always enter the arena from the left, what Stout Mama calls the "sinister side." They go in and out with a cop escort because the crowd would jump them otherwise, especially if they've won against some good guy, kicking him in the balls or conning the referee into a bad call. It's a tough crowd, Stout Mama thinks, listening to some men in green bowling shirts with Snooky's Tavern printed across the back, one saying to the other, "I gotta steel splinter in my finger. You got a knife?" Two grandmothers in polyester pantsuits settle into the front row, their faces calicoed with patches of blue shadow and rouge. They grin at Stout Mama, then flip the bad guys the bird.

The senior usher stops beside her. "The usual blood-thirsty crowd," he says, "blowing their welfare checks for a ringside seat." But what else would they buy? she wonders. What else would so cheaply satisfy their need for vengeance? Here there is bad guys' blood they can smear between their fingers like the squashed guts of social workers putting them endlessly on hold. Here there are no starched collars stamping them failure. Here there are only gladiators and—for just the price of a ticket—Romans.

Stout Mama waves good-bye to the grandmothers, makes her way to the right side of the ring, where the usual mob of kids are begging autographs and pictures from the good guys. Like Buddy Latona who's just returned from Hawaii and sports a tan above his carnival-pink and turquoise paisley tights. Or Jimmy Soul Man and Johnny Pinto, heroes so muscled their torsos ripple even in repose. In their color glossies, their bodies glisten with oil and sweat, luminous as saints in medieval paintings, a flesh so holy that the skinny kids slip up behind and—hesitantly, like touching a live electric wire—put fingertips on a sweaty back and turn away beatified. To be a good guy, thinks Stout Mama, is to enter paradise, to enter the ring from the right hand of the lord.

It's an ordinary paradise tonight, nothing special staged for the grand finale, nothing predictably bloody like a West Virginia Coal Miner's Match with a big pole in the center of the ring and a steel-filled glove attached to the pole's tip. Whichever wrestler shinnied up the pole first grabbed the glove and beat his opponent into what looked like mash. Somehow the mash always resurrected in time for the next week's fight. Miracles, Stout Mama has learned, are as common in big time wrestling as in paradise.

Tonight, the last fight features Pierre the Giant battling two bad guys at once. The program swears the giant eats a dozen eggs for breakfast, plus a pound of bacon and a loaf of bread, washing it down with a half-gallon of milk. The kids shiver with delight, saying they wouldn't want to meet him in some alley, "cause he is UGLY." His cheeks dimple and dimple and slide off into a jawbone like Samson should have had to battle Philistines. His hair stands out all over in a frizz. In his red boots and baby blue trunks, he's an image that would captivate Fellini. Jolly and vacant. The pitiful giant.

Stout Mama knows the crowd is beyond pity. And has to be. Two days before the check comes; breakfast could be just their memories of wrestling bouts to chew like cud. Still, their cheers are with Pierre as he steps right over the ringside ropes, thumbing his nose at Billie Rose and the Pole who have to climb between. For the whole first round, the bad guys only circle the outside ring, sputtering and gesturing defiantly, while Pierre stands in the center, his face dimpled in a perpetual grin. Finally, the crowd jeers the bad guys into the main ring where they buzz around the giant who lunges at them, trying to swat them with his fat palms. Suddenly, they grab his legs from under him, pinning his arms with their feet, beating him in alternate rhythms. Their mouths come down over his face and come away leaving a pool of red.

Stout Mama reminds herself that it's not real, that they must have capsules of red dye in their mouths. That it has to be a setup for continued vengeance like a movie serial, the way the last fight of the night always is—to bring the crowd back next week and line the promoters' pockets with welfare gold. And still there's something in Pierre's fate that mirrors the crowd's reality too well—the outsider that life has ganged up on, the tough guys' pawn.

But the crowd is on its feet, a solid wall of mouths roaring as Buddy Latona and Johnny Pinto leap over the ropes, good guys tearing Billie and the Pole off Pierre, seizing the microphone to taunt them. The bad guys shrivel in the corner, a pair of punctured hot air balloons. The referee pumps the giant's arm in victory but the crowd's not watching. They're climbing on the seats, heckling the bad guys, cheering Buddy and Johnny as they throw down the glove of next week's challenge.

Stout Mama sees the two grandmothers whacking Billie with their purses and the senior usher waving frantically for her to intervene. She gives him a "What can I do?" shrug and turns away, thinking how safe and simple justice is in paradise, where you know the bad guys are always on the left, the hero will arrive in time, and even death can be defeated weekly. And paradise, she knows, is free of cops and ushers. In paradise, you can jump into the ring to kick the devils, touch the angels.

Country and Western

When Stout Mama loses touch with the simple basic truths of existence, she listens to the country and western station to bring her back. Or she goes to Mary Lou's, the local C&W bar. Mary Lou keeps a huge porcelain Chinese good-luck cat above the shelves of bottles. She serves wine in water glasses for two dollars.

Stout Mama is sitting at a table to the left of the band. No one notices her because she does not wear makeup or a bowling shirt. Some nights this can be a problem because Stout Mama likes to dance, but tonight she is tired and only wants to look and listen. The band is playing "Up Against the Wall Redneck Mother." This is one of her favorite songs, but she can never remember the words—only that in one part the singer spells out *Mother*, with a word for each letter. *H* is for haggard, and she likes the pun. She also likes Merle Haggard's songs, the way the lyrics are often about losing, but the upbeat tempo makes you dance right through the depression.

Stout Mama believes that Plato would have called the band's lead singer a "pure form," the ideal shape of country and western. He's about forty-five, with blonde hair in a wave from the forehead where the line's receding, and a hint of sideburns. His jeans are tight, and he holds his guitar a little higher on his waist than rock stars. In a voice a shade less bass than Johnny Cash's, he's introducing the night's special feature, a young woman singer making her debut.

Stout Mama blinks. The woman looks like the platonic form of Janis Joplin, only she's shy and nervous; it really is her debut. Her voice is the platonic embryo of Joplin's—all there, all perfectly formed, but afraid to blossom, certainly too self-conscious to be born. It's just the first song. By the second one, the woman is smiling, and the crowd's polite supportive claps have turned to applause. On the third tune, she takes her first big breath as herself, and belts out Joplin. The nondancers' feet start tapping; even the men in ball caps with the bills reversed sing along, acknowledging the lyrics' truth—that freedom is the same as having nothing left to lose.

Stout Mama looks at the big grin on the young woman's face, the unrestrained toss of her long hair. She supposes that the lyric belted out so joyfully could be called sad. But basic truths are like that, cutting both ways, the kind of losing that keeps you keeping on.

Literary Weight Loss

Stout Mama doesn't understand the science of weight loss. Gaining is easy. The food comes to visit and, like poor relations, stays. Doritos in her thighs, the round blush of chocolate-covered cherries in her cheeks. Maintenance is also clear. The population stabilizes like a small town in Nebraska, and everybody else just drives through on the interstate. But once the food attaches to her bones, how does it leave?

One day after lunch, Stout Mama wanders over to the college library, to the home ec section, which she thinks will be more scientific than the shelves on medicine. She looks up weight loss. This, she reads, means "eating fewer calories than you burn." Stout Mama imagines tiny brushfires breaking out beneath her skin. Perhaps the book is right, for weight loss seems as uncontrollable to her as brushfires. Like an arsonist, she carefully selects her target, but the flames keep taking hold just up the block. To start a conflagration in her thighs, she has to starve her face and breasts to ashes.

Still, Stout Mama finds it hard to understand the logic of such science. She wishes nature were more literary, more Shakespearian, as direct and clear as Shylock's pound of flesh. She knows exactly where she'd carve.

Cigarettes and Mayonnaise

*S*tout Mama has decided to give up cigarettes. The self-help books on quitting, published by her health insurance company, advise her to give her ashtrays to Goodwill, to have all her clothes and her teeth dry-cleaned, to enlist the support of her friends. Stout Mama does not want congratulations from her friends. She wants sympathy cards, wants a good Irish wake, except of course, that would mean plenty of beer and good times, the things she associates with smoking. She thinks that stubbing out her last cigarette will be like breaking off with the best of her old lovers—with someone more reliable than her old lovers, who tend to disappear casually, as if they'd just gone to the store for a jar of mayonnaise in the middle of fixing a tuna salad sandwich, and reappear just as casually ten years later as if the bread were still waiting on the plate. Stout Mama knows her Merit Ultra Lights are more faithfully rewarding, worth even the late-night inflated convenience store price. Stout Mama doesn't care about money anymore, only joy. Stout Mama is over forty.

Stout Mama thinks of cigarettes as decadent and artistic, Marxist and Bohemian, Paris in the twenties. She thinks of herself this way. She worries that when the smoke screen clears, nothing will remain except Republicans and Perrier, the self-righteousness of the born-again. If that's reality, she's willing to lose hold.

But her lungs are less romantic. They think reality is air; they demand a better grip on it. So one morning, she brews a cup of Earl Grey tea and sits down with her last cigarette to say good-bye. The coughing comes as spontaneously as a movie star's tears, and Stout Mama smiles bravely through the end, as confident in her sacrifice as any big-screen heroine. For two days, she sings brave choruses of "Breaking Up Is Hard to Do" whenever her old lover calls. She hallucinates his breath in favorite rendezvous— putting the tea kettle on to boil, pouring the wine into a glass. She sits down at her desk and reaches out of habit for the ashtray, her fingers meeting only themselves, closing around the empty heart of what's become real.

Stout Mama feels frail. She feels maybe reality is something she should work up to, the way she tests a cold lake gingerly with her toes, disliking the shock of plunges. She has never been the sort that dives. She picks a new date for quitting—March 1, safely a month away. And this is a leap year, so the day before will be a good one for sacrifices made to gain some extra earthly time.

Too soon it's February 29. It's 10:00 P.M., and Stout Mama pulls her red Volkswagen into the parking lot outside the jazz bar. Inside, she climbs a stool at the long brass counter. She orders a French wine. She orders pheasant paté. She lights the first of many last Merit Ultra Lights, thinking how far down the scale of tar and nicotine she's slid since the days of her college flirtations with Gaulois. Tonight could be the real good-bye to Paris.

The band takes a break. Stout Mama hears a distinctly French accent near her left elbow, ordering a Remy Martin. Out of the corner of her eye, she perceives a distinctly handsome man. Her paté arrives. "*Bon appetit,*" the accent wishes her. For a moment, she forgets her Ultra Lights. She starts talking to this accent with distinctly dark eyes.

"Where are you from?" she asks, sure of the answer —wasn't she born on Bastille Day? Doesn't she know the left bank of the Seine when she hears it?

"Casablanca." Stout Mama looks down at the counter, at the place where the ashtray should sit. It's there, she's not hallucinating now. But no one really lives in Casablanca, only Bogart and Bergman, playing it again in an old black-and-white habit, the celluloid as patchy as her lungs feel. Still, the eyes that she looks into now are too jet ebony for old film prints, and too real not to have been born somewhere. She'd forgotten that Moroccans often speak French. She wonders why the movie featured Bogart and not a Casablancan local.

Stout Mama stubs her oldest lover into ashes, sure the heavens have offered her some kind of cosmic trade. The last breath of smoke wafts past like time-worn songs she doesn't want to have to play again. She hopes that Casablancans have no word for mayonnaise.

The Honor Code of Crows

*A*gain today the mail is boring: letters from good causes requesting money, catalogs with dual addressees—the name of someone who's lived here before Stout Mama and, below it, the all-purpose Occupant. At the bottom of the box sits the month's fat envelope of coupons: two-for-one pizzas, windshields replaced at a discount, a free introductory week at the tanning salon. The final coupon offers cut-rate body-building classes, pictures a female Arnold Schwarzenegger under the slogan Use It or Lose It. Stout Mama laughs a little wryly, remembering how that phrase used to terrify her when she contemplated her thighs, how she has defused the terror now for years by making the phrase her own, using it to refer to words, not flesh.

Stout Mama calls herself a writer. She would like to call herself a great writer, but she's not sure. She has heard that a poet whom history now calls great once said good poets borrow lines, but great ones steal. She imagines great writers like crows building nests, scavenging the shiny bits that people carelessly

77

abandon. She thinks the greatest writers probably wing about, bereft of conscience, robbing as they will. Because she grew up Catholic, Stout Mama has resigned herself to not being that great. She still associates premeditated theft with sin and the nuns' accusing fingers.

But Stout Mama hasn't given up entirely on being great. Instead, she's made an honor code. When people turn a phrase the way she likes, she advises them to "Use it or lose it," like a firm but good-natured cop telling a speeder that this time it's just a warning, with the promise of a high-priced ticket looming in the future. Stout Mama has found most people are like speeders; they don't pay attention to her warnings. She has picked up a lot of good lines this way —for example, the wisdom of a flirtatious friend at a party, announcing that virginity is lost just once but innocence comes and goes, or the sign on a grammar teacher's icebox, proclaiming herself a rebel without a clause.

Because Stout Mama likes to quote her thefts correctly, she carries a pen and some sort of paper. There are always the extra deposit slips in the back of her checkbook, never dwindling as fast as the checks themselves. Bank accounts, Stout Mama feels, are like bullfights, the matador's sleight of hand with the red—what Hemingway (a possibly great writer?) named grace under pressure.

Tonight, Stout Mama is at a concert by a folk singer named Del Rey, who's introducing a song learned from the inmates in a women's prison. They sang

this in the sewing room, Del Rey says, and they tai-
lored their prison uniforms into high fashion, what
she calls a kind of style under great duress.

Stout Mama makes a mental note to send Del Rey a
warning. She reaches for her checkbook like a happy
crow depositing its latest theft, knowing that these
women show a grace beyond a matador's, a great-
ness that makes Hemingway's a fiction.

A Tango Singer's Arm

Stout Mama is not fascist, but her favorite tune for singing in the shower is "Don't Cry for Me Argentina." In her heart, there's a certain empathy with Eva Perón. In her head, there's a big distance between Juan Perón and Eva. Stout Mama believes that those few women in the past who came to power had to do it differently than men. No votes, no military coups or deals cut in bars. They had to use their wits like Eva, who took stock of any scene fast enough to make herself the leading lady in it. And her looks helped, of course. But not every pretty village girl ends up in Buenos Aires. Stout Mama likes the moment in the musical *Evita* where the tango singer who came to Eva's village, and on whose arm Eva went out of it, is told to be satisfied with having discovered her since that will bring him more renown than his voice. Stout Mama imagines Eva hitting Buenos Aires, how often she must have been confused and scared, and brazening her way through.

Stout Mama knows some legends name Eva saint, and some name her criminal and whore. Stout

Mama distrusts the pronouncements of legends. A boy goes into the woods with his double-barreled shotgun and kills a bear, and the legends say he's just become a man. A girl goes into the city, ends up starring on the palace balcony, and the legends call her a whore. Stout Mama recognizes Eva's failings, just as the peasants who suffered from them did and still called her Santa Evita. It's only the North that likes its saints perfect, unambiguously holy. Stout Mama has a Latin tolerance for human failings. She knows sometimes you can't get out of town without a tango singer's arm.

Stout Mama turns up the volume on the hot water, letting the drops pelt her skin like a warm Latin rain, and begins to sing. It's a fine tune, even in her own off-key rendition. Nobody could write a song that fine about Evita's husband. Stout Mama wouldn't vote for Eva, but she'd ask her to tango.

Failing Nirvana

*S*tout Mama is a news junkie, though she knows the habit is bad for her heart, her blood pressure, her struggles to find peace of mind. When the news doesn't make her angry, it depresses her, which is bad for her thighs. Depression always sends her to the icebox. Still, she's hooked on the habit and hooked on her favorite news addiction: the radio. Specifically, the several hours of news that National Public Radio broadcasts each day. She thinks that NPR is closer to the truth than television or newspapers, even *The New York Times*, which is good for Sundays in bed with lovers and bagels, but not for a weekday diet of facts. She knows that she could locate truth more clearly by subscribing to a multitude of journals like *Mother Jones*, but she has always been a slow reader and the thought of all those pages overwhelms her. And although Stout Mama is often lazy, she has a certain tendency to Type A behavior, liking to do two things at once, a luxury that radio allows her.

Stout Mama rolls out her straw mat, lies down, and begins the series of leg lifts that Jane Fonda has prescribed for fighting cellulite. It's the anniversary of the day the U.S. dropped the first atomic bomb on Japan, and the radio is carrying an interview with the scientists who designed it in a lab in Oak Ridge, Tennessee, a town hardly on the map then, the place full of secrecy—the men not sure what they were working on, their wives knowing nothing. The men being interviewed are asked about the day the bomb was dropped. Stout Mama waits for them to say how shocked they were, how angered and betrayed they felt to find that this had been the object of their research. Instead, the men say everyone came rushing into the lab together; there were parties and booze; they crammed into cars, driving around the town, shouting "fission," "plutonium," "atoms." The men laugh as they recall this.

Stout Mama rolls up into full lotus position, trying to make her mind as blank as these men's. Outside her window, the day continues grey and drizzling, but everywhere else in the nation the weather has been hot and dry. For two weeks, forest fires have been burning out of control. The broadcaster is questioning some men who plan to set a controlled forest fire so they can study the effects of a nuclear winter, when smoke would fill the air like a blanket. "Why not study the fires raging now instead of setting some more?" the reporter asks. "Oh, well," the men reply, "you can't observe much in an uncontrolled situation."

Stout Mama gives up on full lotus. She will never get beyond desire, beyond attachment, beyond this anger. She cradles the phone on her shoulder, dialing

the numbers of her senators, her free hand writing
checks to Greenpeace and SANE/FREEZE, Type A
behavior that she knows is useless, and still it gives
her comfort, like a junkie swearing off the needle at
midnight, knowing the news will be the same
tomorrow at five.

Platform Boots

I t's finally summer, the twenty-first of June. The city's nine-month rain stopped yesterday. Stout Mama is back on her ramshackle porch, the green peeling wood slung out one story above the jungle of weeds and wild rose climbing through blackberry vines that she calls a yard. She's watching the sea-plane traffic from the airport on Lake Union. The lake is very urban, like its name, like teamsters, Jimmy Hoffa, and big biceps, not lily pads and ducks. The planes take off like ducks, a little ungain-ly, the way a mallard seems to run along the water, flapping till it's airborne. The engines roar with World War II movie sound effects. There are two petitions circulating in the neighborhood: one to trash the planes and their engines, one to keep them on the lake. Stout Mama is the only person who has signed the second petition.

Stout Mama is supposed to be working, to be writ-ing poems. But she's tired of the noise that poems make, more tired still of the noise of poets. Watching the tiny planes with their cartoon Snoopy and the

Red Baron double wings, their pontoon feet like oversized galoshes, Stout Mama makes a mid-life career decision. She decides to pilot seaplanes.

Stout Mama has never flown in anything smaller than the propjets of Ozark Airlines, planes noisy enough to leave her ears as stunned as five hours at a heavy metal concert, but much larger than these seaplanes. She has never piloted anything but her red Volkswagen—which she secretly believes can fly, but has never tested this theory. Stout Mama does not have a good record of managing either wind or waves. In kayaks she panics at the immensity of blue, swelling around her. In sailboats shorter than twenty feet, she consistently capsizes, first to one side, then the other. But Stout Mama has read that mid-life decisions are nothing if not adventurous, that she who indulges in self-doubt is lost. She looks up flight schools in the yellow pages, but none of them lists seaplanes, and by the time she begins to dial their numbers it is after five o'clock; Stout Mama remembers that office hours do not stretch like daylight with the season.

Decisions make Stout Mama restless. She pumps up the tires on her bike and rides it to the north end of the lake, where an old gasworks has been converted to a park. She likes to read the graffiti that boys spray paint on the rusting machines, climbing over the high barbed-wire fence around them to write messages like Jay Loves Heather Forever. Somehow the bravado of this always makes her feel hopeful about the future, about the way these young men use a word like love so much more freely than the

ones of her own generation, even make the effort to
climb dangerous fences to proclaim it in Day-Glo
letters, so much more satisfying than anonymous
initials on a tree.

The artificial hill the city has built beside the gasworks is almost deserted: only one man settled on
the top as if he meant to wait there like some druid
till the midsummer sunset. The man is very tall and
very thin, very tanned, dark haired, and chisel featured, with the lines of the chisel just enough askew
to save him from the cover photos of *Esquire*. The
man is Stout Mama's favorite list of adjectives for
men. She rides, then walks her bike around the hill,
again and again. Stout Mama is shy but not subtle.
She thinks this combination often comes together,
that the signal of a wallflower is more insistent than
the bright aggressive grins of Farrah Fawcett
blondes.

Eventually, it works. The man begins to talk. He says
he rode a bike through Mexico, up the hills of
Chiapas. Stout Mama is impressed. She is out of
breath from this artificial green bulge, and she
knows the hills of Chiapas are really mountains, has
crawled up them herself in a second-class bus, the
engine straining with the weight of crowded aisles,
the windows leaning out on sheer drops.

"And what do you do now?" Stout Mama asks,
knowing this is always a good, if unfeminist,
approach. Get them to talk about themselves. You
can train them later.

"I work on the lake," he answers. "I fly seaplanes."

Stout Mama has, of course, read Shakespeare's play about Midsummer Night's Eve. She knows that strange and magic meetings can occur on this date, but she is still surprised. And even more surprised because the man is offering to take her on a private flight tomorrow.

Tomorrow dawns perfect—a cloudless day so blue the sky turns almost deeply lavender. Stout Mama climbs up on the plane's slim strut as it bobs in the waves and fastens herself in the cockpit. Already life seems different; already she feels like a bush pilot in Alaska, no flight attendants demonstrating oxygen masks, no air traffic control—only the ducks diving away, the engine roaring through the spongy plugs in her ears, the pontoons skidding over the waves till they're up and the boats are suddenly small flashes trailing silver wakes, the landscape a map of toy-sized places. She was right about her Volkswagen's ability to fly. This plane feels like a Volkswagen, ramshackle and loud, low-tech and chugging, the small shudder of small power that keeps her up and moving, so little between her and the air, the tangible sense of air, of being alive inside it.

They leave behind the dense mosaic of the city, the pods of skyscrapers, the sinister grey of Navy ships in harbors. The distant range of mountains becomes blue ridges, cradling the plane's small cicada-bodied shell. Stout Mama wants to hover here forever, between the waterfalls dropping into valleys, between the glaciers where the man says pilots used to land,

carrying supplies to survey teams. She thinks of the
writer Isak Dinesen, who went up in a small plane in
Kenya. Later, the Africans had asked her if she'd
seen god. When she answered no, they seemed to
think the flight a frivolous one. But this, Stout Mama
thinks, is all she need of gods and goddesses, all
she'll ever need of anything.

They head for Mount Olympus, seeming to fight the
air toward it for a long time, like someone running
in a movie toward a camera with a wide-angle lens,
like Dustin Hoffman at the end of *The Graduate*, chas-
ing the bus carrying Katharine Ross. And suddenly
they're past it, swinging back too soon, too fast, the
sadness that Stout Mama always associates with
coming home. The man beside her picks up the
microphone, talking to the other pilots in the dots of
planes that she can see now, working out a rhythm
of landing. The plane curves past the houses of the
rich on the lake's east side, the ducks diving away,
sun setting on their left, the pilot bringing them in
slowly, smoothly, expertly with grace to touch and
then surge in the waves—the conductor bringing the
last violins to a sweet swell—and the plane is taxiing
into port.

Stout Mama looks up and sees the tall man beside
her stretching to see over the instrument panel, to
scan the lake for swimmers and boats. She looks
down at her own short legs, dangling above the
floor. She understands mid-life decisions may need
more than courage, that her spirit's reach is longer
than her bones'.

"Don't worry," says the pilot, flashing her his tanned smile. "There's a woman here who flies for us who wears extenders on her shoes."

It's the evening past midsummer and the days are shortening into winter. Stout Mama waves the pilot another good-bye as his motorcycle climbs the hills home. She climbs into her Volkswagen, starts the engine, and begins her lists above the takeoff roar: a long white silk scarf, goggles, a thick pillow, and platform boots.

Fourth of July Flags

*A*nother bad week for news. Each day the
Supreme Court has decimated somebody's rights.
First civil rights, then the rights of a woman to the
privacy of her own body. What they've left in place
is the right to burn a flag. Stout Mama has a friend
that went so far left that he turned the corner into
libertarianism. She understands that this last flag-
burning decision is not an inconsistency in the
court's pattern, merely the turning of that corner into
a grey space, neither left nor right. But the right
wing that the court represents is less insightful; all
day the president has been wrapping himself in the
flag, vowing to make amendments to protect it.

Stout Mama thinks of bikers with flag bandannas,
of Mick Jagger strutting in the cloth of the British
Empire. She thinks how much small matters matter
in the politics of her country these days. She drives
to the grocery to buy food and wine for her friends
coming over tonight to watch the fireworks display
from her porch. At the checkout counter, she asks
the cashier whether the store sells flags. He's not

sure, but the young girl bagging groceries says they do and says the store is sold out. It's the Fourth of July, after all. "Too bad," Stout Mama says. "I wanted to burn one." Everyone in the checkout line stares. "Well," she says, "it's the only right we have left." And the bag girl finds her a tiny one, the sort of flag on a toothpick you use to decorate cakes.

After the fireworks, Stout Mama lights the flag. And marvels at how little time it takes to burn out.

Enough! or Too Much

Whatever Stout Mama likes, she wants more of. She has, in the jargon of self-help books, an addictive personality. Beginning a good novel, she finds herself anxiously counting the pages left, hoping the author's sequel is already at the press. Saturdays, she listens to her favorite radio program, "The Royal Canadian Air Farce," a half hour of political satire that leaves her depressed, picturing the week she has to get through till the next joke. The Fourth of July is even more difficult. No matter how long the fireworks last, no matter how spectacular the display, with pyrotechnics imported from Japan exploding in computer-sequenced patterns, it is never enough. While the crowd gathered around the lake applauds the display's finale and the boat horns blast their approval, Stout Mama focuses on the last glowing cinder, like a child wishing on the evening star, and begs for more.

This trait makes choices agonizing, especially in big American cities like the one Stout Mama lives in, where everything is offered in at least twenty-seven flavors. Sometimes Stout Mama wishes there were only chocolate and vanilla. In a restaurant, the menu paralyzes her. She drops out of the conversation, closing her eyes, imagining each entrée, its tangible textures and tastes and smells. Whatever she finally selects feels like a sacrifice. Or she opens the weekend entertainment guide and finds five movies she's dying to see, two concerts, and a dance performance, plus the weather forecast looks good and she's been meaning to go camping. Sometimes, it's easier to stay home.

This trait makes shopping perilous. She finds mangoes on sale at the market, but it's the height of strawberry season, and the first of the blueberries have just come in. She brings them all home, where the speed at which they rot outstrips her ability to consume them, and this oppresses her. Then she overcompensates and lets the kitchen run on empty, nothing but moldy oranges and milk. Some foods she's learned she can't allow inside the house, like taco chips or bittersweet chocolates, things she'd binge on, standing at the kitchen counter in a kind of trance, her hand automatically seeking her mouth until she scraped the bottom of the bag.

This trait has been hard on her quest for thin thighs. It has been hard on her lovers. It has been hardest on Stout Mama's heart. In her opinion, a good man should consider love addictions healthy and non-threatening. As the old songs warn, he's a good deal harder than taco chips to find.

Stout Mama has been writing her own song. Like all hit tunes, the words are few, the message simple:

"Love attack. La la la la la la la la la la. Love attack."
She hums it as she contemplates the possibly good
man coming over tonight, the expanse of time she'd
like to spend indulging in his menu—the weeks on
each earlobe, the months on his short graceful
hands, the years to ask him questions, argue with his
answers or agree.

In the man's apartment, she has seen a copy of a
drawing by William Blake, with a small figure at the
foot of a ladder reaching up toward the moon, and
under it the poet's wish: "Enough! or Too Much."
Like a gypsy reading fortunate tea leaves, Stout
Mama feels optimistic. She knows the slogan of an
addict when she sees it.

~~~~~~~~~~~~~~~~~~~~~~~~~~~~~~~~~~~~~

ID

*T*he Chinatown section of Stout Mama's city is called not Chinatown but the International District, a somewhat misleading name evoking images of Croatian groceries with Sudanese and Argentinean clients queued up at the checkout. In actuality, the name reflects the mix of Asian residents and businesses, a reminder that the East does not belong entirely to China. Locally, the district is known simply as the I.D.

A late-night theater performance has just ended, and Stout Mama and her friend are looking for a place to have an after-the-show drink. Stout Mama always loses her bearings in the I.D., and her friend gets easily lost anywhere. But eventually they stumble on the one spot that still seems vaguely open. Downstairs, the restaurant has closed, but music drifts from the upstairs bar where a spotlight is shining on a small stage, on a heavily made-up woman in a stiff kimono.

Stout Mama and her friend sink into chairs facing the stage. All the other tables are empty, except the corner one with three thin Japanese men in business suits and thick-rimmed glasses, silently chain-smoking. Stout Mama and her friend turn their attention to the kimonoed woman. It's not her voice they're hearing; she's lip syncing to a taped song. And "woman" doesn't seem to be her ID. Stout Mama and her friend cannot be sure. They know how easily they lose direction in their own city, and neither one feels capable of transcultural accuracy in pointing out cross-dressing. The kimono mimes the song's end, disappears into the darker recesses of the bar.

Beside the table, a smaller figure in less elaborate Japanese traditional dress is speaking Stout Mama's name. Stout Mama looks up into the face of a former student, the waitress, taking their order for wine. Somehow this makes Stout Mama feel even less secure, as if she were sixteen again, as if she'd made it safely past the bouncer at the door with her fake ID, only to run into some friend of her parents.

The music has started up again. One of the businessmen has claimed the stage, lip syncing the microphone. Behind him, on a big screen, Japanese characters appear in sing-along fashion but without the bouncing ball. Above the characters, a video of melodramatic images complements the song: solitary young women staring wistfully into space, solitary young men smoking wistfully in cafés. The distinctly older men waiting at the table for their lip-sync turns support their chins on elbows and take long wistful Marlboro drags.

The wine arrives, and it's a common California red,
as exotic as apple pie. Stout Mama and her friend sit
confidently back and lift their glasses like two travel-
ers picking up their passports at some border
crossing, the customs ritual passed, the foreigners
now comfortably international.

Learning about Hurricanes

To escape the cool grey days of rain that September brings to her city, Stout Mama has taken a vacation to Hawaii, to the garden island of Kauai where she can at least prolong her summer for a week. She arrived on Wednesday night. Thursday was summer. Friday she is learning about hurricanes. She has been learning about them since 6:00 A.M. when the police bullhorn woke her, announcing that everyone should evacuate low-lying areas. Stout Mama's area is, of course, low-lying, a hotel chosen for its proximity to the beach, its view of the waves.

Stout Mama is a night person and does not make decisions well at 6:00 A.M. She has been pacing her room unproductively, wondering whether to pack her bikinis for the evacuation to a shelter or leave them in her room like a talisman, a pledge of faith that the room and the beach will still be here when the hurricane has passed. While she paces, she chain-smokes, glad now that her attempts to quit have always ended in failure; she takes comfort in gripping the familiar filters, like holding a friend's hand in a horror film. She checks the morning talk shows on the television and learns that hurricanes come in five ascending degrees of intensity. Her hurricane is a four or five, depending on which channel she tunes into. She learns that her own degrees of panic increase whenever the civil defense people being interviewed say "Don't panic." This is especially true when they tell the audience to follow the civil defense procedures listed in the front of the phone book and her phone book doesn't list them. Perhaps the island prints a special directory just for tourists, with those pages omitted—some Chamber of Commerce attempt to paint the local skies as consistently sunny, the breezes always gentle.

A man from the hotel staff comes in and makes her decision. He props the mattress against the sliding glass doors that face the beach and tells her to evacuate to the shelter at the local community college. "Take everything with you," he cautions. "The building might not be here when you come back."

Because Stout Mama often teaches at community colleges, she is ambivalent about this shelter. She thinks such colleges are shoddily constructed; she knows the pay they give her is shoddy. On the other hand, they have sometimes been her refuge in financial storms. She loads her rental car, wishing she had opted for full coverage insurance, glad that she has already given the car a name, a practice she thinks establishes some mystical connection, a protection the non-mechanically-minded use against breakdowns. She hopes that such protection extends to hurricanes. At the college, she positions the car as far as possible from the tall metal lamps and trees that ring the parking lot.

Stout Mama learns that shelters on an island of perpetual summer are mostly filled with tourists. She learns that tourists can be politely, even cheerfully accommodating, as long as they're afraid. This accommodation does not extend to smoking. The smokers identify each other early on and form the kind of camaraderie only a despised minority can form. She learns that smokers stay outside the building, huddling under covered walkways, until the winds reach eighty miles an hour. After that, they go cold turkey. Inside, Stout Mama learns that everyone has been territorial except her. Every chair has been claimed and most of the floor, leaving only narrow passageways. When the night comes, she will have to hunch beside a doorway in the fetal position.

But the hurricane arrives before night, the sky still pale though the rain whips in sheets across the ground like driven sand across a beach. The wind rips pieces of roof from the other buildings, and clumps of pink insulation dot the fields like soggy cotton candy. Stout Mama watches the public art sculpture on the wall of the courtyard, a circle of metal that curves into giant jagged prongs. She imagines the wind behind it, the tourists it could impale. Already the TV is dead, the local radio station's off the air, and the Honolulu announcer says they've lost communication with Kauai. "The hurricane," he says, "is poised to engulf the island; a warning siren will sound and then everyone should crawl beneath a table or a mattress." There are no mattresses in the shelter, there are not many tables, and the only siren in Stout Mama's ears is the pressure of the wind.

Standing beside the door, Stout Mama listens to some parents tease their children, saying the winds would blow them away. As a short person, Stout Mama has been the brunt of such teasing all her life. Now she's tempted to test it, to dash out into the field. Would the winds really sail her like a kite? She watches a station wagon rock, watches the hunks of metal roofing flip by, end over end, and knows the answer.

The power goes, and then the water supply. The winds grip the shelter, gusting well over one hundred miles an hour, and suddenly stop. In the eerie quiet of the storm's eye, the air floods with golden light, a gentle peace descends upon the campus. The tourists grow brave and many grow less accommodating. They divide into categories. The disgruntled ones complain about the loss of their vacation, the lack of civil defense organization, the stench of toilets that can't be flushed with the water cut off. The harbingers of doom speculate about the devastation, the days it will be till the airport's open. The rugged individualists insist on roaming the courtyard even after the eye passes and the winds gust from the opposite direction, defying the harried efforts of police to herd them inside.

Stout Mama tries to pass as local; she attaches herself to some islanders. When the dawn comes, she will do the same, will steer her talismanically unscathed car beneath dangling cables, through the road's embroidery of power lines and branches—a slow zig-zag between fallen poles—back to her hotel where the roof and sections of the third floor will be missing. "Want a paying guest who'll help clean up?" she'll ask. And the staff will say, "Don't pay, just help us." And she will.

The Pangs of Love

A hurricane is like a fierce dance, the *duende* of a tango or flamenco. The winds encircle the eye, the insistent grip of a lover, crushing a partner's ribs. The hurricane that embraced Kauai was called Iniki. In the Hawaiian language, *iniki* means "to pinch, sharp and piercing, as wind or the pangs of love." Before the winds hit, Stout Mama had seen a young woman, hardly more than a girl, with her soft girl's knees dimpling beneath pink baggy shorts. She was gathering the fragrant plumeria blooms that had spilled from a tree. "To make a lei," she'd explained. "Well," Stout Mama had suggested, "you might as well take the blossoms on the tree too; they won't be here tomorrow." Stout Mama had meant to sound cheerful; she sounded cynical. But the woman had just smiled. The tree was thickly branched and rich with flowers. They knew it was too beautiful to touch.

The winds arrived. And arrived. And rested languorously around the eye's calm center, and arrived again. In the civil defense shelter, the young woman curled up with her blonde boyish lover on a raft of blankets. Stout Mama curled up with her sweatshirt for a pillow. The full moon pressed a little light through veils of clouds—enough to frame the silhouettes of fallen palms. Everyone dreamed of something.

In the morning, Stout Mama watches the lovers pack up their homeless blankets and the can of brown-tinged plumeria blooms. In the morning, she hears that the sugar canes have been flattened, the coffee plants stripped of beans, 90 percent of the buildings damaged. In the morning, Stout Mama can feel nothing at first; the landscape is too surreal like the goose honking in the courtyard of the community college that served as shelter. The reports seem too dry, all documentation, news data, distant as a nightmare she knows she ought to analyze, and can't. Then she catches sight of the plumeria, stripped of blossoms and branches, a sturdy skeleton still hanging on, its roots sunk deep as an old love. The kind of love it hurts to meet and lose and meet again years later. The pain of something beautiful you used to know.

Frames of Reference

*A*cross the street from Stout Mama's hotel is a store called the ABC, a small place, just over the mom-and-pop size, selling souvenirs and booze and the kind of groceries tourists buy for snacks. It is the first store in the area to open after the hurricane. The morning it opens, a long line immediately forms. Stout Mama is bailing water from a flooded bedroom along with Carol Ann, a young woman who works at the hotel. "Just look at that line," Carol Ann says. "It makes you think you ought to be in it. Like there's something they already know we'll need."

The next day, Stout Mama's job is to stand in line for the needs of herself and the hotel staff. She has a list: beer, canned tuna fish, licorice sticks, several brands of cigarettes, diet soda, rolls of film to document the damage for insurance adjusters. She has her gear: suntan lotion, a hat, a book—the essentials for standing hours in a line in tropical sun. Today, she's lucky. The line moves quickly while she gossips with two guests from the Westin Hotel. They spent the hurricane packed into a ballroom, watching the chandeliers sway. When the hotel reduced its room rates to a post-storm "bargain" of $110 a night, they say the guests revolted and won the right to stay for free. Stout Mama thinks the hurricane was politically conservative in its targets. She knows the average islander is suffering, but as far as she can tell, the luxurious Westin didn't sustain much damage. She does not say this to the Westin guests, only husbands her space in line ahead of them. In less than two hours, she's hauling the goods back to her roofless hotel where the staff reward her with a trip to the beach.

The beach lies in front of the Westin. The sands and the waves are public, but now that the airport's finally open and most of the rich guests have fled, the few employees that the Westin has not laid off patrol the access. Stout Mama has to take the public route, a climb down lava rock steps, a wade across a shallow river. The beach is nearly empty, a situation that Stout Mama relishes when she's reading in her chair, regrets when she takes her contact lenses out to brave the sea. And so today she mostly reads, interrupted only when a man with a gold chain around his neck stops by to comment on how fine the weather's been since the storm. Stout Mama agrees. "I work for ABC," the man says. "Oh," Stout Mama replies, perking up. "I spent the morning in the line before your store." The man looks nonplused. "ABC," he says. "It's a TV network." And moves on.

The Balcony Queen

tout Mama prides herself on packing light. Beside her desk, she keeps a drawing of a turn-of-the-century girl in a straw boater and pleated skirt, surrounded by luggage and steamer trunks, with the caption Running Away. Stout Mama knows that this is not the way to run. She packs light—a bag that can be coerced beneath an airline seat or into an overhead bin. A bag she can count on. A bag that does not have to be checked.

Such packing is not easy. It takes hours of planning and lists, of sacrificing purple and forest green items for a few bits of black and beige that can be mixed and matched together. Stout Mama is lucky; over time, most of her wardrobe has become some shade of mauve. For her trip to Hawaii, she packed only a few clothes. But she included three swimsuits, in ascending degrees of style: a simple black-and-white two-piece for sunbathing on her solitary lanai; a skimpier garden floral bikini for snorkeling on the beaches where she hoped to stand out from the tropical fish in the eyes of interesting men; a one-piece cut high in the thighs, deep in the décolletage, the one she calls her Mediterranean yacht suit, reserved for occasions she has yet to encounter, but is always optimistic about.

The night before she left for Hawaii, Stout Mama ate dinner at a friend's house. Ate pasta and a slice of decadently chocolate cheesecake. She could feel the calories bulging, her thighs expanding like a hot air balloon. She pictured her flesh blimping outside the swimsuits. She kissed good-bye her dream of Gidget Goes Hawaiian after Forty.

Stout Mama, of course, hadn't counted on the arrival of the hurricane. And hadn't known high winds can leave priorities as radically changed as landscapes. Dragging a heavy sack of drenched drywall from her damaged hotel, Stout Mama understands that extra fat can be relied on in food shortages, that Gidgets weep like helpless tourists in the traffic jam to the closed airport, and that over forty means you leave the heaviest bags of drywall for the younger crew to tote. She understands she has packed too many clothes for a hurricane. She's been living her nights in the same shorts and tank top. Who can tell when the only light is the full moon and candles? She's been living her days in the black-and-white swimsuit whose white is steadily turning the same rust-red as the soil she sweeps and hauls.

She wanted to be queen of the beach. What's left of the beach is mostly deserted, the sea a temporary refuge from work, a place to take a salty bath until the water starts flowing again in faucets. Stout

Mama shifts her goals. She wants to be useful. Still, she feels a failure. When she cleans a room, the woman in charge comes by and wipes the mirrors again. Today, she's sweeping the walls of the hotel's balconies, the leaves and purple blooms of bougainvillea that the winds have driven into the stucco's white. Her hands blister under the broom handle. The blossoms fly and stick to her swim suit, to the sweat that drips between her neck and navel. But the walls turn back into white. "Good job," the woman tells her. "You're really the balcony queen."

Reasons for Not Traveling

The first three times Stout Mama traveled to other countries, there was an earthquake half a globe from wherever she landed. It became a macabre joke. "Let me know where you're going," her friends said, and folded their Rand McNally atlases to see where they shouldn't live. The next trip, a war broke out in her zone and a political assassination happened across her street. Now she's tried her own country, taken a brief vacation to Hawaii, and a hurricane has hit. As always, Stout Mama has emerged unscathed. Even her rental car has come through without a scratch, sitting between the smashed windshields on either side of it. Stout Mama thinks that maybe she shouldn't travel. It's so hard on the rest of the world.

Just a Draft

*W*hy don't you come over tonight, he said, as Stout Mama was driving him to his car to drop him off. And she said is that a proposition, and they both ignored the question while he gave her directions to his car. And he picked up her hand then and said the proposition still stands. And yes she said I will. And was glad when she got there that they had a bottle of wine meant to be given to a mutual friend. And didn't think she was showing him much when they finally hit the mattress. Just taking it easy. It had been a long time for Stout Mama, a couple of years since she'd had some love, and that was only a one-night-stand man doing a second night to wish her good-bye. She was used to clipping the hairs around her nipples only to visit the breast cancer surgeon for her check-up. But sex is like riding a bicycle, some skill you never forget. She was taking it easy, she thought, no showing off, no look Ma no hands on the steep downhills. He didn't think that. He was sort of ruefully glad and worried the next morning. Like, this was a revelation he said. Like, I'm pretty busy and can't see you. Stout Mama was nonplused,

thinking she'd let the door swing open just a little,
to let a small draft pass, knowing the difference
between that and real wind. He was a small straw,
the kind that falls in a wolf's first tiny huff. She'd
been hoping for brick.

Wholesale Crystals

Stout Mama has a habit of eavesdropping on conversations in bars. She often does this after movies, the sort of movies you go to alone because no one else will spend $6.50 to see them. She has just been to an Almodóvar movie that, like most Almodóvar movies, treads a fine line between sexist macho and the mockery of sexist macho. Her favorite part was some fake ads that the heroine created for a product called Ponte panties. The ads maintain that the panties have chemicals turning farts into perfume, particles that absorb urine when you have to pee and can't find a bathroom, and, on solitary nights, the panties can be rolled up into something reliably erect. Stout Mama can identify with all these desperate situations.

She has more trouble identifying with the conversation beside her. An intense young woman has been telling a table of maybe less-than-intense types about her writing. And now she's linking that to crystals. She knows this woman who does something that she calls a "crystal layout." "You lie down," she says, "in a Christ-like position, and the woman lays the proper stones about your body." She has done this, she says, and the experience was profound. It made her know her writing was profound. So profound, she says, that she went home and couldn't write, only make some popcorn and watch TV. But she knew that the piece she'd been writing was "very extremely important."

On both the sublime and ridiculous levels, Stout Mama associates profound experiences with the sixties—the Zen conundrum of one hand clapping and the Doonesbury cartoon spoofing those stoned exclamations: "Have you ever looked at your hands? I mean, really looked at them?" She associates crystals with the ersatz profundity of the century's end, a sort of Marin County take on the esoteric side of capitalism. And she's right. "The crystal lady," the young writer says intensely, "didn't know anything about stones when she started. But she studied. And now she's got a business selling them wholesale."

Stout Mama's Dreams— Number 113

*S*tout Mama is getting married. But to whom? And the caterer's assistants keep spreading place settings on the floor that's dusty and scattered with pine branches. "I'm going to report this to your boss," she tells them. But who is that? And where is she or he? She knows the ceremony will take place somewhere beyond this tiny niche she can't quite squeeze through. It will happen soon. She has only half her gown on and that half is already smudged. No makeup, and she ought to have combed her hair. It's time. She wonders, did they pick a minister? A minister? Surely they didn't, must have written their own vows. She can't remember writing anything. She can't remember any rehearsal. What is she supposed to say? And to whom?

With It

$\mathcal{S}$tout Mama wants to be "with it." Not in everything. She does not want to wear layers of all-black clothes, pierce her nose for a ring, and put three more holes in each ear. She would like to dye her hair a startling purple, but she doesn't want to bleach it first, and her hairdresser swears that's the only way to get a truly startling shade.

Still, she wants to be "with it." At least musically. She does not want to be locked into whatever tunes compose her generation's equivalent of Guy Lombardo and his champagne waltzes. She knows she was "with it" in the sixties and seventies, even a little into the eighties, but lately she's lost touch. She recognizes rap, booming from the extra-bass speakers of the cars beside her at the stop lights, but she can't define hip-hop, can't name the difference between heavy metal and grunge. For years, she's been listening mostly to the jazz station. But jazz, for all its innovations, is a timeless sort of genre, as classic as Beethoven. It is not a way to stay "with it."

Stout Mama begins to tune in several times a week to a public radio station run by students at the local university. The format is highly varied and definitely "with it." Stout Mama tells herself she doesn't have to like everything, just try to understand it. This can be difficult if she happens to tune in early on a slightly hung-over morning and gets heavy metal. Then she tells herself it's the circumstances, not old age, that make her wince. The metal is no heavier than the rock of her youth, those tunes by Led Zeppelin or Iron Butterfly.

Stout Mama knows about digital sampling, about the plagiaristic ways that sounds can be lifted now from a recording and stitched electronically into new songs. She has a good memory for music. She can hear a guitar riff on the latest CD and name the Rolling Stones tune it was lifted from. She is trying to be "with it," but she wishes for a beat more complicated than rap's, for electronics more like Hendrix. She supposes her preference for original solos over electronic copies is probably purist. She supposes her preference for the artists who burned their hearts and lives out creating those solos is probably romantic and decadent. She understands enough about the new hip attitudes to know that romantically decadent is out, jadedly decadent is "with it."

Stout Mama has been depressed lately—maybe it's age, maybe it's the autumn coming on, the start of a new school year, all those student essays waiting once again to be graded. Driving to class, she fiddles with the car radio and hears the wail of a guitar she recognizes—an old hit by Jackson Browne—

"Running on Empty." Down and out lyrics, but the singer's not sad, and her own spirits are lifting. She thinks of the younger man she's been dating, how he seems prematurely riddled with middle-aged neuroses. She thinks he knows nothing about really running on empty, about the freedom of that state. She pulls into the school parking lot as the music shifts to the Beatles song, "Don't Let Me Down." She lets the motor idle in her parking spot, listens till the end.

Three hours later, Stout Mama starts the drive to her second teaching job. She's ready to leave the radio dial on the oldies station she's lucked onto, but they're having a spate of commercials and she starts fiddling again. She finds a station specializing in an earlier era, the hits of her high school days. She remembers slow dancing in the gym. Actually dancing in couples. But not like the fox-trot. More erotic. More swivel in the hips. More grind. Stout Mama thinks maybe it was this that marked her generation, made them a bridge between the parents that danced in more decorous couples and the younger set that separately thrash. Love in the sixties was free, but there was something innocent and passionate about that freedom—like the politics of the time. Nothing jaded, nothing cynical or slam-bang.

Stout Mama notices her mood has been steadily improving as she regresses in musical time. She wonders about this. She doesn't remember her youth being all that joyous. But maybe compared to middle age. The Supremes come on, take her over the last cloud into sing-along joy, into the wisdom of what their mamas said about love—that it can't be hurried and it never comes easy. It's a game of give and take. She's handclapping off the freeway, through the free right turn at the exit's light, into the parking lot and her office. She's sure that there are timeless rhythms and she's with them, turning in step on the stage like The Supremes in their high-stacked hairdos and tight glittering gowns. She knows how to run freely on empty. She knows nothing comes easy. She just hates to be let down.

Puta Brujas and the Moon

When the scented candle sputters out, Stout Mama lights her jack o' lantern once again, once again burning her hand. She thinks it's some unwritten witches' rule—that you have to sacrifice a little flesh before the carved face glows. Stout Mama and her women friends appreciate the ways of witches; they have their own witchy attitudes, designed for dealing with the late twentieth century in the United States, where the conservative backlash now paints feminists as bitches, uppity flesh that should be barbecued on stakes. With a whimsical disregard for Spanish grammar and a fine sense of male attitudes toward independent women, both north and south of the Rio Grande, they call themselves the *puta brujas*—the witch whores. Their aging bumpers carry stickers that read My Other Car Is a Broom. In their sprawling city, they live in the same zip code, making it easy to convene spontaneously around a cauldron of cheap wine. The liquor seethes with modern witch talk, politics footnoted with references to National Public Radio. The *puta brujas* think the news analyses by Nina Totenberg are witchily incisive; they wish she'd run for president. They spice their talk with cigarettes like frog legs tossed in for flavor. They laugh about a line in *Eleemosynary,* a play they've just seen. The actress said that smoking makes you feel forceful, letting the people you're with know you want oral gratification, but not necessarily from them. They know it's attitudes like this that give them the title of witches; they know what that title rhymes with. They have a *puta*-ish disregard for easy rhyme.

The rain lets up a moment, and the half-moon is suddenly bright behind the clouds that trail across it like the skirts of women on uppity brooms. The moon's light torches up the fall leaves scattered in the wet street and the faces of the neighborhood kids that haven't bothered with costumes but still ring bells, expecting treats. Stout Mama sets her pumpkin's one-toothed grin into the window, turns back to the table, her place in the coven, where the talk has turned to potions for diminishing the power of testosterone. "We could put the potion in the water supply," Stout Mama says, "like fluoride. Better living through chemistry." She grins like a Cheshire pumpkin, lights another frog's leg.

Relations with Christ

Stout Mama flips the pages of the job application asking for her work experience, her awards and references, her relations with Jesus Christ. Her relations with Jesus Christ? She knew the university was Christian, but she'd had no idea they'd ask for some pledge of faith, some oath of loyalty to the victims of Roman crucifixions. She considers writing that she watched the hours of *Spartacus* on TV, despite the constant commercial interruptions, despite the bad dialogue and the silly dimple in Kirk Douglas' chin. Maybe she should say her Catholic family had Christ over every Friday night for fish sticks. Maybe she should tell how breaking up was hard to do. And worth it. She considers lying; she wants this job. She considers taking the high road, explaining that she's nondenominational but full of ethics, that she still supports the Sandinistas, writes checks to Greenpeace and the New El Salvador Today Foundation, that she recycles and sends postcards to Congress protesting against scandals and the cover-up of scandals. She consults a Jewish friend who gives her an answer she knows is theologically confused but semantically perfect in its ambiguity. Under the question about her relations with Christ, she writes "immaculate."

The Fruits of Granola

It was in a bar in Canada—in Victoria, British Columbia, a sleepy town like any small-town capital tends to be when the governmental body is not in session. Only the rose-streaked sky was in session now, and Stout Mama had been standing on the corner, ignoring the changes of the stoplight, standing there so long she saw the bearded drunk on the steps across the street grinning under his cab-driver cap, acknowledging he knew she waited there, like him, just to watch the sun go down, the night's event.

Stout Mama gets drunk only after sunset. This time in a bar in Canada, climbing up on the stools that are always too tall, giving her order to the bartender with red hair and a good smile, reaching for her wallet to pay. That was when she met Samantha, when she noticed that, like her own, the young woman's wallet was held shut by a rubber band. She knew they shared the same tolerance for tacky, the same reluctance to replace a keepsake, the same lack of will to take the time, the money, the trouble to change a thing worn out.

125

Samantha was drinking B-52 shooters, a combination of liqueurs Stout Mama savors, and notices that hip young people chug. Samantha was under thirty, all black lace and leather, and decidedly hip. They started talking about their wallets.

Samantha was a sixties' baby, the kind who'd grown up on no money, on love and dope and flowers, politics and rock. "What didn't you like," Stout Mama asked, "about being a hippie's kid?"

"The whole-grain bread," Samantha laughed, "and that healthy granola."

The bar was closing down, the redhead with the good smile buying the last round; Samantha's friends had long disappeared. Stout Mama made the offer of a lift home, knowing she'd get lost on the unfamiliar streets back to her hotel, knowing she and Samantha would never call the numbers they'd exchanged. Knowing that what mattered was this trust they'd validated for each other—how they'd all turned out all right, these hippies' kids and women old enough to be their mothers, holding themselves together like wallets with rubber bands, the good sweet ripeness buoyed up like plump raisins on those mouthfuls of granola.

Stout Mama and the Black Orchid Man

For years Stout Mama hasn't read the comics. But as a child she read every strip in the Sunday paper, scattered on the Midwest farmhouse floor after Mass and the ritual roast beef midday dinner. Her parents liked Dagwood and Blondie. Her brother idolized Steve Canyon, affecting the same black turtleneck sweaters, spending hours in the bathroom shaping his crewcut to match Steve's. Everyone read Mary Worth. But for Stout Mama, the most important strip was Brenda Starr, that beautiful redhead with the fabulous clothes—a character Stout Mama now thinks of as an anomaly in the 1950s of her childhood: an independent woman with no family and a good job. A job for which she was well paid and well respected: everybody called her "the star reporter." She was star writer, star detective on the trail of justice and the truth, star of travels, risk, and adventure. Things were happening in the world and Brenda Starr had a right to be there. Stout Mama didn't dye her hair red, but she took the star reporter as a model, a one-way ticket out of the decade's scene of two kids and a husband, two cars in the garage and a washer/dryer.

Along with Brenda came her lover, the Black Orchid Man—as mysterious as the patch across his eye, as elusive and rare as the flower he was named for. Months, even years might pass between the lovers' brief, intense encounters, but the idea of him was always there in the background, like a promise. Looking back now at the shapes of romance in her own life, Stout Mama thinks maybe he wasn't the best model for a lover, but at the time that she chose Brenda, it had seemed like a package deal.

Like Brenda, Stout Mama has had her affairs, but only one Black Orchid Man, the kind you name in capital letters the day you meet him, and every lover after that is lowercase. Stout Mama and her Orchid Man have had their brief, intense encounters, losing track of each other sometimes for years, then a call comes or a letter, a knock at the door, a few days' rendezvous in some East or West Coast city, never in the steamy jungles of the orchid. This is, after all, the geography of real life, not comic strips. And real hearts, Stout Mama has found, have moments of weakness, of wishing that romance might stretch beyond the number of frames dictated by the size of newsprint. Still, she knows a chosen myth is not just something to live up to, but an explanation for the way things are. In weak moments, Stout Mama has taken comfort in remembering that this is how love goes between such independent beings as orchids and stars. She knows enough psychology to know that this is rationalization, a way to glamorize the lonely nights. She thinks delusions of grandeur are better than no delusions at all.